NO PLACE TO LAY MY HEAD

Anthony Richardson

SAPERE
BOOKS

NO PLACE TO LAY
MY HEAD

Published by Sapere Books.

24 Trafalgar Road, Ilkley, LS29 8HH

United Kingdom

saperebooks.com

ISBN: 978-1-80055-703-1.

To
John and Nicky

TABLE OF CONTENTS

FOREWORD
by
OTTO HEILBRUNN

During the last war Russian units fought on the German side against their own country. Not many of them were assigned to combat duty since Hitler had decreed that the privilege of bearing arms against Russia could be granted only to Germans. Yet a number of German officers in the field felt otherwise. They thought that Russia could be beaten only with Russian help and Russian companies were employed by them, particularly in the fight against Partisans. Not all of these companies proved reliable: one company of Cossacks suddenly mutinied, murdered the German N.C.O.s and then escaped to the other side; as a result all the other Cossack units with the Germans were withdrawn. But others fought on to the end, no longer on the Russian front but in Italy and France. One of these men is Sasha Nioman, whose story is told in this book.

He was not a Russian proper but a Byelorussian who at the outbreak of war lived in eastern Poland. It came under Soviet rule in September, 1939, when Stalin occupied this part of the country. In June, 1941, the Germans attacked Russia, the Russians hurriedly withdrew and for the next three years the Germans were in control of the territory.

Within the short space of a few years the unhappy country had changed its master three times. Not all of the populace who joined one of the opposing sides in the German-Russian campaign did so for ideological or idealistic reasons. Some were motivated by opportunism and many by the force of circumstances. The Nioman family affords a tragic example of

9

the latter: Sasha's elder brother, yielding to Communist pressure, joined the Partisans, and Sasha himself volunteered for the Wehrmacht's anti-Partisans in order to forestall German reprisals. There was no cause for loyalty or for remorse when sides were changed later on.

A number of guerrilla fighters have published their memoirs, but surprisingly enough the experiences of the anti-guerrillas have rarely been described. The present book thus fills a gap. But the book is more than a moving story of short-lived triumph and agony. During the last sixteen years there has hardly ever been a period without a Partisan war, with its theatres somewhere between the Philippines and France, Norway and North Africa. Its importance as an instrument of modern warfare can therefore hardly be overrated. The book makes us realize how much may depend in a future Partisan war in enemy country on the massive support of the anti-Partisans of enemy nationality. The present book thus has merits quite apart from its literary qualities. It has the stamp of authenticity and is a most valuable and timely addition to the literature on guerrilla war.

INTRODUCTION

This is a true tale and Sasha Nioman, whose story this is, now lives at Brighton happily married and with a family. He works as a machinist in a factory. I met him in the way that writers so often encounter their characters in biographies of this kind — the victims, you might say, that swim into the author's ken and eventually disappear into his maw! A brother-brush, a well-known playwright and scenarist was approached by a friend who told him with some considerable zest that he had run across a story that was unique and enthralling and which would, in his opinion, make an excellent film. The friend was told in reply that the material must first be put into some coherent shape and form before it could be turned into a picture-continuity, and that probably the best way to go about the business would be to pass the victim and his material along to some accredited biographer who might be prepared to handle it in the form of a book, from which first step the later development of a scenario might arise. My name was suggested and a meeting was arranged. The result of that meeting is this book.

Nioman is not Sasha's real surname. Only twice since the war has he been in touch with his family, with the brief news of them which is given in the last pages of this story. Moreover, Dubrova is not the name of Sasha's village. Nor can we print a photograph of "Papa," though Sasha has one, because it could be through the obvious channels a possibility that a copy of *No Place to Lay My Head* might find its way through the Iron Curtain and into that eastern province of Poland. It might be that some objection, real or otherwise, might be raised by those in authority. It could very well be that a swift and terrible retribution would follow. That is unthinkable; so these small points have been deliberately suppressed.

But otherwise this is the truth in all essentials. There has been no attempt to mince matters on my part. What I have described through Sasha's eyes and mind are the things that Sasha as a mere boy, not seventeen years of age, saw and suffered and survived.

There must be scores of Sashas in the world, the little, humble, unsung heroes of whom any nation would be proud. For my part, I can only reiterate what I have often said, and that is I am sorry that Sasha was on the other side, but if things had been reversed I am positive that some of those late comrades of mine with whom I had the honour to serve would have been well pleased to have discovered him as a member of our Squadron and that alone, amongst old soldiers whatever their race or age, is the chief praise that they can understand and seek no further.

In conclusion I must express my thanks and gratitude to Dr. Otto Heilbrunn for his valuable Foreword and for his great trouble in reading and advising me on the text, and to the Librarian of the Imperial War Museum and all her assistants who have been of the greatest possible help.

ANTHONY RICHARDSON

London, January, 1957.

PART ONE: FARMER'S BOY

1

Sasha sat up in bed. He was suddenly fully awake. In the far corner of the bedroom he could see Nicola's truckle bed against the wall and the hump of his oldest brother's buttocks beneath the blankets. Nicola was snoring, a soft rattling intake and then the sibilant sigh of escaping breath. The sound always reminded Sasha of that other terrible night when Mamma had died in Papa's arms; the low death rattle deep in her throat, and then the last expiring whistling breath that had seemed as if it would never cease. Only then, when there had been utter silence in the room, had Papa collapsed into that uncontrollable, horrible, and strangulated outburst of tears. In his hopeless grief he had rocked himself to and fro beating at his temples with clenched fists. Nicola and the second boy Walter had led Papa through the doorway, each supporting him by an elbow. Little Valia had been asleep at the time in her cot and had known nothing of it all. Sasha had stayed by Mamma's side and lifted her hand where it trailed towards the floor and placed it palm downwards on her breast. It had appealed to him as a holy, reverent and fitting gesture, strangely impersonal. At no time had he himself wept. It was as if he had been emptied out like a bucket, and there wasn't anything left inside him. Now looking back to that autumn of 1939 he thought it was just as well that Mamma had been called away. He himself was sixteen and a half now, in 1943, just over three years later, and sickened with it all.

This was the hour. The Partisans never came before midnight. Up to that time he could sleep quite soundly, and then as twelve o'clock approached he would begin to stir, till of a sudden he was awake, and however cold the night might be, bathed in a perspiration that his home-made linen pyjamas never completely absorbed. Thereafter he would lie awake, waiting for that dreaded sound of warning, the swish and rustle of the sledges' runners and the rubber-dub-dub of galloping hooves. After that terrible things could happen.

So it had been ever since that Sunday morning in the summer of 1941 when the Germans had attacked their ally Russia and the Russians had fled at the first bombing of the nearest railway centre at Baranovici. They had abandoned their weapons from rifles and machine guns to heavy artillery. The Byelorussians of the district had hurriedly hidden them. Sasha himself knew where one precious rifle was hidden in a wood. Three days later the Germans had entered Sasha's own home town of Haradischa, not a hundred miles west of Minsk in Byelorussia.

From then on as the Germans had advanced more deeply into Russian territory and the lines of communication had intolerably lengthened, the Partisan movement behind the German front line had steadily gathered weight. It was particularly strong in the region where the widower Papa Nioman lived with his three sons and small daughter on his farm a mile from Radzimichy. When the Partisans struck the occupying German forces made reprisals on the civil population. Those who favoured the Germans, the Partisans in turn destroyed.

It was cold sitting up in bed. The great five foot tiled stove in the centre of the wooden house must, Sasha thought, be in need of fuel. Clearly the alternative was to lie down again and tuck the bedclothes round his ribs. Instead he dragged a blanket round his shoulders and sat with his legs drawn up to his chin, intently listening. It was just as impossible to lie down as it was to refuse to listen.

This was the nightly terror; the cold and deadly suspense that caught at the heart and numbed it, that destroyed all feeling. It was not so bad in the daylight because then he could steal away from the farm and make his way through the orchard that surrounded his home and the out-houses and climb the small hill which was crowned with the little wood. There concealed by the trees and the brambles he would scramble to the disused fox's earth where the rifle, in its carefully oiled rags, was hidden with its boxes of ammunition. He had picked both up in the meadows by the river near the old Fort where they had been flung amidst the summer wild flowers eighteen months ago. Whenever he had the rifle in his hands and stroked the smooth butt with loving fingers, or better still, thrust it into the muscles of his shoulder, he felt no semblance of fear for any living man. Sometimes he would dare to slip a round into the breech for devilment and bravado and fire a single shot into the air. But in the dead of night in the quiet of the house the awful dread returned.

Somewhere, very far away under the moonlight and across the gleaming moonlit snow, a dog barked. So still was the night and so rare the icy air that it was difficult to judge how far off the sound might be, but it brought Sasha out of bed. He tiptoed across to Nicola and shook him by the shoulder. Nicola grunted and swung round sulkily on to his other side.

"They're coming," said Sasha. "Get up. Get up."

"All right, little brother," said Nicola, at once awake and aware of the urgency in the younger lad's voice.

"Put a blanket round you," he added. "And get some slippers on."

He groped under the bed for his own. When he stood up he was nearly head and shoulders taller than Sasha. He was twenty-one years of age and looked older; broad and stalwart where Sasha was slim and wiry, but both had their father's russet coloured hair and the bright sparkling eyes of their dead mother. In the next room Walter tossed restlessly beneath the sheets but by the wall his father slept on soundlessly.

Sasha joined Nicola by the uncurtained window. There was frost on the single glass ventilation pane and Nicola rubbed with his thumb and made a spy-hole. Then he laid his arms round Sasha's shoulder. Outside the moon was high in the sky and in places the snow sparkled as if it had been sunlit. There was no sound at all now, with the frozen world holding its breath. Then again a dog barked till the barking turned into a dismal, high pitched howling that seemed to Sasha like all the tormented souls in Hell. He pressed close to his brother and Nicola's fingers tightened on his shoulder. There was an affinity between these two unshared by the rest of the family.

"I can hear the horses," said Sasha.

Nicola raised the forefinger of his free hand. His head was cocked on one side, listening. He nodded.

"Yes," he said softly. He drew in his breath deeply.

The sound was quite distinct now. The watch-dogs had ceased their howling but the beat of the fast trotting hooves was unmistakable and like an undertone was the whisper of the sledges' runners.

"Two lots of them, at least," said Nicola. "They're coming this way again. Are you scared?"

"No," said Sasha. "I'm not scared when I'm with you, Nicola. And I'm not scared when I've got my gun. Let them come."

"You'd better mind that gun of yours," said Nicola. "If the police get wind of it —" he referred to the German field-police of occupation — "we'll all get shot."

"They won't find my gun," said Sasha. "No one will find my gun. It's up in the wood with the ammunition boxes. One day I'll need that gun, if it's only to give it away to another like Vanya Krachankoff, the artillery man. If I hadn't hidden a rifle for the time that Vanya needed one he'd never have been able to start the Partisan Group round Radzimichy."

"So when the Partisans pay *us* a visit — when our turn comes," said Nicola mockingly, "When they come to steal *our* corn and pork to carry away with them, then I'll tell them my little brother Sasha Nioman is a good Partisan such as themselves since he started the movement here and then they'll put the food back and not make us join them nor question us about the Germans and leave us alone. That's all we ask, isn't it, little brother, to be left alone... Dear Mother of Christ, why can't we be left alone.... *They're here!*"

They were drawn up in the roadway outside the gates of the farm. There were two pairs of horses and two sledges. When a horse threw up its head the bit clinked in its teeth. It was clearly audible to the watchers in the room; so were the muffled voices of the sledge crews.

There were four men in the first sledge, and five men and a woman in the second. All wore sheepskin jackets and leather belts. Three carried *ruchnsi-puliemot* — the light machine guns with the round magazines on top, stolen from the Germans. The men's caps were pulled down to their ears in the bitter night; the woman wore a shawl over her head and half across the lower part of her face. She looked like a witch. The steam rose off the sweating horses and blew in vapour out of their nostrils when they snorted. They pawed the ground with their calkin covered hooves, so that the dry snow rose round them in puffs of white dust. The stars in the dome of the purpling sky glittered like diamonds and the brilliant disc of the moon could have been etched with acid.

They had all got out of the sledges by now and appeared to be arguing. It seemed to Sasha watching, that it was a strange thing to do to come down from their hidden encampments in the dark, silent, sinister forest with its frost-creaking trees and ice-crackling branches, without having decided upon an objective and made a plan. If he were a Partisan or a leader of men, even if — which God forbid! — he were forced to be a German soldier, he'd be certain that he had some sort of a plan before he came out into the open and risked his life. That was just common sense.

The woman was pointing directly towards the window where the brothers watched. A man in a lambskin cap who stood before her continually shook his head. Sasha could see the woman clearly, short and squat, with the broad Mongolian features of flattened nose and heavy lidded eyes. He instinctively backed aside as if he could be seen as she moved her gloved hand again, but Nicola's grip on his shoulder tightened.

"They can't see through," said Nicola. "But if they do come this way, we must wake Papa and Walter. I'll leave it to you to see that Valia doesn't take cold. Wrap her in a blanket."

"Very well," said Sasha. "How I wish I had my rifle."

"For the love of God," said Nicola. "No more talk of this rifle of yours. If they come tonight keep a civil tongue in your head, else that's the end of all of us."

But outside they were clambering on to the sledges once more. The woman was the last to heave herself above the runners. Then the drivers were jerking the reins and the leathers were slapping against the horses' haunches. The little cavalcade swung off the road on to tracks that led to the farm opposite. Only a matter of two hundred yards off Sasha and Nicola could watch their progress all the way. They saw the sledges draw up, dark coffin-like shapes against the snow with a man at each pair of horses' heads, and another posted alongside him with his *ruchnsi-puliemot* at the ready. Without further ado the rest of party strode resolutely towards the main door of the house. The man at the horses' heads jerked the bits and withdrew with the sledges to the rear of the building.

Thereafter for some minutes they were lost in the shadow of the shallow porch; then a torch flickered on for several seconds and as suddenly went out. In its hovering spotlight Sasha thought he could discern the dark silhouette of the tall man with a lambskin cap who had argued with the woman before their own gate and thought he heard through the freezing crispness, a dull sound of an imperious thudding on a door. A yellow square from a window sprang into being and a slit of light in the porch widened to a broad beam, then flooded the doorway. Dark figures, huddled and intermingled together, hurried across it. The porch went into black darkness and as a curtain from inside was hastily drawn across the window that, too, disappeared. Beyond the beating on the door there had been no sound of any kind since the first sign of life from within.

"They have gone to Petroff's place," said Nicola. "They will take their full. He has salted pork in plenty."

"And then — ?"

"It depends what happens — inside."

"I would shoot them," said Sasha, "if they laid a hand upon what was mine. Partisan or German they are both enemies to me. I would tell them —"

"There is only one argument with a man with a gun, little hothead," said Nicola. "And dead men can't answer back and that lesson's easily learnt."

For fully half an hour silence and darkness reigned in the little homestead opposite. Years before in the first days of the Polish occupation each small-holder had been allotted his six hectares in the scattered village. All that might now be happening behind the four walls could only be conjecture. In some ways it seemed to Sasha that the suspense and ignorance could be worse than the reality. There was never on such occasions any aftermath of confidences, merely rumours. Caught between two fires neighbour could never trust neighbour. There were bidders from both sides for secrets at the price of coin or blackmail. No man could trust another and informants were themselves spied upon in turn. The night itself was less dark than this tortured, twilight world of mistrust.

The first indication that the work in hand had been satisfactorily completed was a renewed intermittent flashing of the torch in the opening doorway opposite. There seemed to be a struggle taking place in the porch but when two men emerged into the moonlight Sasha could see they dragged heavy sacks, and a third following staggered under a great side of bacon. There was a sudden shot from the back of the house where the horses waited and when the woman appeared she also appeared to be lugging a smaller sack behind her, when she abandoned it, as she did as soon as she reached the fence at the end of the garden plot, it crumpled into an untidy heap.

She rolled it over with her foot before she moved towards the horses.

"I was told," said Nicola softly, "that Petroff's youngest son could stand the strain no more."

The last man to leave the house carried a bundle of clothes arid a roll of blankets under one arm. In a little time both sledges were loaded and with their crews aboard moved off at a walk. When they reached the road they turned to the left towards the mill by the bridge and the old Fort. As they passed Sasha could see one of the Partisans, head back, holding the neck of a bottle to his bps. When he lowered it the woman dashed it from his hand. It fell from the sledge as the horses broke into a trot. The drumming of their hooves grew fainter in the distance. By the fence of Petroff's farm a small dark bundle lay quite motionless in the snow. No one came out from the house. It was as if they had been given a time-limit before they might leave. But at two o'clock in the morning, when the Partisans opened fire with their machine-guns on the police station at Radzimichy from the grass ramparts of the old Fort and the German field police returned their fire so that the tracer-bullets arched their way criss-cross through the moonlight, only then did a woman emerge from the homestead opposite. She made her way towards the fence as if instinctively she knew where to find that which she might be seeking. She made no attempt to lift the body but knelt in the soft snow beside it. Once she raised her hands as if pleading to the sky. She only rose to her feet when a crimson trickle of fire suddenly appeared beyond the fence along the near wall of the storage barn, where the delayed action incendiary candle had at last burst into flames. Then she called to those within and men ran out.

In the bedroom in Sasha's house, Nicola turned from the window. The former was shivering.

"That was Sergei Petroff's mother," he said.

"You are cold, little brother. Come to my bed. We shall be warmer together."

He swung his legs under the blankets and Sasha crept in beside him. They put their arms around each other.

"Sleep," said Nicola," "I am here."

"We shall always be together, you and I," said Sasha.

"By the grace of the Holy Saints," said Nicola. "If that should be God's will."

Within minutes Sasha slept. But it was not till the night was but two hours from dawn that Nicola turned on his side. He lay till then on his back, his arm protectingly across the young boy, whose head lay upon his breast. So Nicola remained motionless, his eyes open, listening to the other's gentle breathing, and staring into the moonlit recesses of the bare room. Sometimes he murmured inaudibly beneath his breath: "But sooner or later our turn will come... sooner or later." Outside the night was very still again, nor had at any time the rest of the household awakened.

2

Sasha was chest high amidst the bracken in the wood behind the orchard when the Germans made their visit at half-past nine the following morning.

He had risen with the rest of the family at six and breakfasted in the living room where Papa Nioman slept on his folding bed. Walter who taught in the local school at Haradischa was as dark as his mother had been but his eyes were weak and he wore glasses. He was an earnest young man and was considered by the family at nineteen as their intellectual superior. Papa, with Nicola and Sasha farmed their dozen hectares. Papa had been born on the land and knew his work. He was short and broad with rusty red hair that matched his face when he was half way through his litre of vodka. Sometimes he stirred black pepper into the spirit. He was known to have stated he preferred his tipple with a bite to it. Valia at twelve, with her auburn hair and blue eyes was a beauty.

Over the meal of white cheese and bacon, ersatz coffee and coarse bread, Nicola said:

"They were out visiting again last night."

His father shrugged his shoulders. This was no news. No night passed these days but an incident occurred. It was not to be expected that it could be otherwise. Nevertheless mere courtesy prompted him to ask indifferently: "Who was it this time?"

"They called at Petroff's."

"I heard nothing," said Papa. He had long lost interest in his neighbours. Since the unexpected death of his wife at the age of forty he had almost completely withdrawn into himself. Suffering years of religious prosecution under the Pilsudski regime he had grown as a Byelorussian to hate the Poles and all they stood for. His wife and family and his farm had contained his world. When war came and his wife died in the autumn of the same year and the Russians and Germans carved up Poland, that world had for many months ceased to exist. In his grief he had nearly died. When in the later stages of the Russian occupation he had seen whole families disappear overnight, spirited away, separated and destroyed he had grown indifferent to a fate which could just as likely be his at any time. The Poles he had loathed. When the Russians came he had hoped for a change for the better. With their deportations and systemized slave-labour he had tasted the dregs of bitter disillusionment. Whole villages, men, women and children, had been ordered to work on the autostradas, the great motor-traffic ways that ran from north to south. The farms became neglected, the cattle starved, the pigs grew lean and the com rotted. When the Germans invaded in 1941, he was glad. There could be no change for the worse. It wasn't possible.

"There was an accident, I think," said Nicola.

"I think it was Sergei," Sasha blurted out. "I couldn't see for certain. It looked like a little bundle in the dark —"

"We shall hear in good time," said his father bitterly and pushed back his chair.

Valia began to cry. The tears rolled out of the blue eyes and down her cheeks. She made no attempt to check them nor brush them away. She sat and wept till Walter rose and drew out his handkerchief and mopped her cheeks, murmuring words of comfort. She caught at the lapels of his jacket and pressed her face against the harsh cloth. Papa watched the scene with an expressionless face. It was beyond him to commit himself to any words of reassurance. He knew their worth.

"Come," he said to his eldest and youngest sons. "There's work to do."

Nicola and his father went out to muck down the pigs and the four cows. Sasha crossed to the wooden stable on the left of the orchard. The snow was deep round the boles of the cherry trees and the branches shimmered with ice. He carried a kerosene lantern, for the dawn was as yet only a grey hint in the sky and it would be dark in the stall where the pony was kept.

Once inside he hung the lantern on a hook above the manger and, taking a curry-comb out of the rack by the corn-bin, began his grooming.

Inwardly he was quaking. The enormity of Sergei Petroff's swift and terrible death, accustomed though he was to this long reign of terror, appalled him. He had known twelve years old Sergei not in a comradely fashion but as the boy that lived next door and they had met in the fields and talked. Now the Partisans had raided Sergei's house and had killed Sergei. Why had they killed him? Had he lost his nerve and attempted to escape an interrogation? Had there been a quarrel, an unlucky blow? There was no telling. One fact only remained. Sergei was dead.

It could have been himself. Beyond the orchard, across one meadow, at the top of the knoll beyond, there was a wood. In the wood was a fox's earth, and within, a forbidden rifle. Did anyone else beside himself and Nicola know that it was there? Had anybody at any time seen him handling his precious possession? It was a terrifying thought.

He ought to have been more careful, more discreet. The feel of the thing had given him such confidence that it must have gone to his head. If the Partisans knew of its existence there were no ends to which they would not go to extract the secret. Was that why Sergei was dead? On the other hand, if the Germans found it, their anger would be still more terrible, the punishment inevitable. It would not fall on him alone. It would include the entire family, even Valia. They would be made to dig their own graves under the muzzles of the German automatic rifles. Then they would stand before them and a German officer would take his Luger out of the leather holster. Sasha could almost feel the cold nose of the pistol on his neck, at the base of his own skull. It was reasonably warm in the stable, but the exertion of his grooming could scarcely account for the perspiration that broke out all over him. All of them could be killed, for his own folly.

At the very first opportunity he must rid himself of the incriminating evidence. At the very first opportunity, as soon as it was first light he would go up to the wood and he would take a spade with him. Then he would place both rifle and ammunition in the fox's earth and carefully fill it in. Only then would he feel safe. He laid down the curry comb on the bin and looked outside. The sky was growing light, a soft and pearly grey. Nearby a cow was lowing and there was the clanking of a bucket. He would swear Nicola to secrecy about the rifle. No one else knew.

The sun came up as he completed grooming the pony. It looked round at him as he patted its rump and it nibbled at his sleeve. He slapped it twice under the belly for luck and the pony twitched its tail with pleasure and cocked a rear leg in a playful half-kick. Sasha put on his sheepskin jacket and drew on his gloves. There was a spade and some clean rags over the way in a corner of the barn. There would be nobody about; they would be finishing with the pigs and the milking and then Papa and Nicola would likely enough get busy in the grain-store. Walter would have set off for his day's teaching and be well on the way to Radzimichy by now and Valia would be busy in the kitchen. He would be able to finish off the job in the wood in half an hour without anyone knowing. He was beginning to feel better already. He began to whistle.

As he slipped over the threshold of the stalls he came face to face with his father.

"You can do this for me," said Papa.

He held a wax-threaded bodkin, an awl and the two ends of a broken crupper-strap in his hand.

"It broke yesterday. I shall probably need the cart today and the saddle always rides up on Krischa's back if the crupper isn't tight. I don't want a pony with a sore back. Get on with it right away."

There was nothing to be done but comply. Sasha trudged back through the snow to the house and went in by the back. He took off his gloves but kept his sheepskin jacket on. It would save time when at last he could move to the wood. He felt quite certain now that he had decided upon his plan that every second was precious.

There was little necessity to hurry unduly, but the fear which had returned to him in double measure made him feel awkward. The awl became clumsy in his fingers and once he nearly ran the bodkin into the palm of his hand. He couldn't get the vision of four able-bodied males and one flame-haired girl with the brightest of blue eyes standing before mounds of freshly turned mould, with shallow trench-like holes immediately before them, out of his mind. Any more, although the sun was mounting slowly, than he could dismiss other hateful memories that recurred to his mind. It seemed that nightmares were not confined to those hours between dusk and dawn.

He could remember when as a boy of thirteen he had been taken into Baranovici with Papa and Nicola. There had been trouble getting the necessary permits from the Russians. The town — the nearest railway centre — was a great contrast to Radzimichy with its four small streets with their wooden houses and the wooden church in the centre square.

The day had nearly been ruined when he became separated from the others in the busy crowds and found himself lost. He had kept his head and made for the railway station, because it was a recognizable central point from whence he could retrace his steps. But in the tangle of streets he found himself at length confused and wandering down an embankment skirting a railway siding. It had been his intention to follow the line back into the station.

Seven closed cattle trucks had been standing in the siding. They had appeared to be half derelict, unpainted, and the apertures rather than windows, placed high under the planking of the roofs, were covered with wire-netting. Dusk was falling and the seven deserted trucks in the neglected siding had seemed even at first sight peculiarly forlorn. He had paused wondering why they should be there when a sudden sound emanating from the one directly opposite to him struck like a dagger.

It was a long, tremulous moan that could never have come from any animal. It rose in pitch like a tremolo on a flute, utterly heartrending and desolate, the hopeless, unforgettable cry of a soul in utter anguish. Then to Sasha's amazement the grisly chorus of the doomed and abandoned was taken up by other voices. They came from the interior of the truck and, awed, he ventured closer.

The stench as he approached caught at his throat and nostrils like a mouthful of poison gas. Then he saw that the lower planking immediately above the floor was saturated and dripping, and that where in places the liquid ordure and putrescence had dried, a green and whitish crustation rimmed the damp, dark patch of its shame. And now the occupants of the other six trucks took up the refrain, and faces so emaciated and drawn that they scarcely appeared to be human fluttered momentarily at a netted aperture, then fell back and were immediately replaced by others. Once he saw a skeletonian hand clutch at the netting and hang there as might a bird's claw, and once a fearful mask emaciated to obscenity croaked a plea for water. He turned and ran nor stopped till he reached the main station.

That night Nicola explained to him that the entire male population of a neighbouring village had, ten days ago, been removed to work in the salt mines. It seemed that nine of those days must have been spent in a siding.

The crupper-strap was mended at last. He seemed to have taken twice the time which he would normally have done. The job reflected little to his credit. He inclined his head listening anxiously. There seemed to be no one about except Valia, moving amongst her pots and pans. He left the house, crossed to the stable where he placed the strap in the bin, and made his way up through the orchard towards the barn.

The morning was advancing. He judged it to be getting on for nine. Whatever happened he must at all costs reach the wood on the knoll and bury his rifle. Enough time, Heaven alone knew had already been wasted. His conscience was like a scourge.

He found the spade and rags where he had expected to find them, tucked them under his arm and set off for the wood. If anyone should question his solitary snow-tracks he could explain, feeble excuse though it might be, that he intended since the weather was dry to collect kindling.

Though it was the middle of January, he was surprised to find the wood so bare. Moreover, the brambles seemed to have withered and become less impenetrable though his former trips had seldom been made in daylight but rather at the first fall of dusk.

Then the wood had seemed friendly and confiding. Now in the sunlight it seemed as transparent as a wire birdcage. Nevertheless in places the thorn clumps were of considerable height.

The fox-earth was just inside the first belt of trees. He made directly for it, stepping high and daintily over the bramble bushes and using his spade to support his progress. He saw the opening at once though it was partially filled with snow and lying full length on his face thrust his arm in the hole until he could feel the butt of the rifle. It was still there, all right.

He drew it out and laid it beside him. Its backsight and breech were bound with rag which he removed. Then he slipped the bolt and looked through the barrel. It was none too clean and needed a pull-through. He rose to his feet so that he might catch the sunlight the better, moving a little more out into the open, swinging the rifle this way and then the other. The barrel flashed dully in the sun.

The feel of the rifle in his hands was good as always, like the presence of Nicola, it gave him confidence and courage. He squatted on the ground with the weapon across his lap. The pull-through must wait, but he re-covered the breech and magazine with clean rag. Then as he rose to his feet to pick up the spade he saw with dismay a single approaching figure stepping across the fence not a hundred yards off.

It was Ivan Zavada. Sasha recognized him at once. He had known him distantly for years, an overgrown, handsome fellow, whose methods and morals had never been beyond reproach. Neither of them had ever been friends, but they had never been enemies. Now at twenty-three, Ivan, his manhood achieved was reputed to be eager to prove his worth. There had been rumours that he favoured the Partisans.

For the moment Sasha was stunned at the discovery of the other's approach. On the spur of the moment, caught off guard and dismayed he in the sudden impulse flung the rifle from him, towards a thicket.

It fell into a tangle of thick thorn which immediately closed and swallowed it. That the ammunition in its box was at least safe in the fox-earth flitted through Sasha's mind as Ivan ranged alongside.

"Good-day, Sasha Nioman," said Ivan Zavada. "You seem to be busy."

Sasha shrugged his shoulders. There was nothing to do but make the best of it, and bluff it out.

"There is always plenty to do," he said.

Ivan's glance fell across the younger man's shoulder, travelled beyond, searching.

"If I'm not being too impertinent, what's this job you're on?" said Ivan, and he was smiling as if he were enjoying a joke all to himself.

"Collecting kindling," said Sasha sullenly, but even to himself the tones of his voice sounded unconvincing.

"With a spade?" asked Ivan, touching with his foot the implement where it lay on the ground. Ivan settled his cap more to the side of his head to suit his taste. Then he smiled again.

"There is no reason why you and I shouldn't understand one another," he said.

"No reason that I know of," said Sasha.

"In fact," said Ivan, "a little plain speaking might well clear the air. Where's that rifle I saw you handling a moment or so ago?"

"Rifle?" said Sasha, with all the assured innocence he could command though his bowels were turning to water.

"Sometimes in the evening, about dusk," said Ivan Zavada, "I have heard the sound of a shot in this direction. There are admittedly at almost every hour in this accursed countryside noisy sounds of explosions and shots. But very seldom at dusk which is usually a quiet period. And as I need a rifle particularly badly within the next few days, I should be very glad to receive as a gift from your good self, the rifle I saw you handling and which is the one no doubt I have heard you practising with. Is the rifle in good order, Sasha Nioman?"

"I don't know what you're talking about," said Sasha and there seemed a great vacuum below his ribs.

"You know perfectly well what I mean," said Ivan. "Somewhere in this wood — not very far away either — a rifle is hidden. If my guess is correct it could be one found after the Russian retreat, and before the police had combed the district properly. No doubt you were lucky to discover such a rifle and have kept it since for yourself."

A quarter of a mile away, crystal clear in the early air, a voice was calling.

"Sasha, Sasha... Where are you?"

It was Nicola's voice and there was a note of urgency in it.

"My brother's calling for me," said Sasha. "I must go."

"Your brother means nothing to me. Where is that rifle?"

"I don't know," said Sasha desperately, and that for the moment at any rate was partially true.

"Then I suggest you find out," said Ivan viciously.

The voice in the distance was growing closer.

"Sasha... Come at once... it's urgent ..."

"I'll not be bullied by you," said Sasha. "Why don't you learn to mind your own business, Ivan Zavada, as I mind mine!"

"Very well," said Ivan. "Now let me make myself quite clear about this. I need that rifle because I am joining a friend of mine shortly, and a rifle is the price of my admission ticket to the select and secret order to which I wish to belong. I shall call back tonight at midnight. I know the room in which you sleep with your brother as there are a great many other things I know. I shall flash a torch at your window three times and that will be the signal that I am waiting. I shall expect you to meet me outside with the rifle in your hands. Have you any ammunition as well?"

Nichola's voice close at hand, broke in:

"Where are you, Sasha, the police are here! They want to interrogate us all... Sasha... it's about last night!"

"Ah," said Ivan gently. "How very interesting! Of course you would have seen what happened at Petroff's place. As for the police, it was on the tip of my tongue to remind you of their existence. Because if that rifle of yours isn't in my hands just after midnight tonight, an information will be lodged with the Commandant of the "Shutz-Politzei" in Radzimichy that one known as Sasha Nioman is harbouring arms despite the regulations and that *not only himself but his entire family is guilty*. And that, of course, will be most unfortunate for those concerned. So till midnight then —"

He turned on his heel and plunged silently into the heart of the wood, disappearing among the trees, as Nicola short of breath and panting, broke into the covert, saw his brother and gasped:

"Didn't you hear me calling? Don't you know it's madness to keep those brutes waiting? Oh! you'll be the death of me. Come now.… come now, quickly. They want to know what we saw last night … we must give no one away and tell the same story.. pick your feet up. What's the matter with you? You look as if you'd seen the Devil himself!"

3

There were three of the German "Politzei" in the sitting-room as Sasha entered with Nicola. The "Unteroffizier" was interrogating Papa. The other two their thumbs tucked into their leather belts, their legs straddled, stood nearby. All three were heavily armed, with revolvers and rifles. The "Unteroffizier" was taking notes.

"You heard nothing?"

"Nothing!" said Papa sourly. "I go to bed to sleep."

The sergeant swung his arm before his face and brought the back of his hand across Papa's mouth. "Keep a civil tongue in your head," he said. "Is this the youngest son, who sleeps with the brother?"

"That is correct," said Papa, wiping his bruised lips.

The interrogation lasted an hour. It was quite apparent to Sasha that very little of the evidence they gave was believed. Rather it was implied that much which they could have told was being held back.

There was a deal of shouting and gesticulating, combined with threats and insults. It was all to no avail. Neither Nicola nor Sasha disclosed anything which could lead to identification of the raiders.

By eleven o'clock it was snowing.

The flakes were small at first and swirled downwards almost vertically through the still air, but before very long most of the footprints in the farmyard were obliterated and up in the wood on the knoll the already overburdened boughs sagged and sighed and from time to time allowed small avalanches to slide down through their leafless twigs and tumble to the ground.

Down in the pig-sty where Sasha was helping to kill a pig for the larder his thoughts were far from the buckets of boiling water and brine, but very close to that self-same covert where the snow by now would be making every thicket and thorn bush look alike. Very soon the pall of white could conceal all traces of a rifle which had been thrown hurriedly away in a moment of panic. It could indeed be lost for many weeks to come. It could certainly still be missing by this midnight. The thought was completely terrifying.

Late in the evening Luba Kumovich called. She was sixteen and the daughter of Vasil Kumovich, a cousin of Sasha's who was in the police, and lived in the neighbouring village. Whenever Luba came into Sasha's presence he was deeply stirred. Her hair was in long blue-black plaits tied with two scarlet ribbons and her skin was delicate and flawless.

She shook her cloak and stamped her little feet in the hall to get rid of the snow before she came into the house and Sasha who had met her at the door found his hands trembling when he folded her wrap and placed it over a chair. She made no attempt to disguise the reason of her late visit. She was frightened. When they had boiled a little milk for her and sweetened it and settled her down in the living-room, they managed to get the story from her.

Four men had been arrested by the "Shutz-Politzei" in her village during the morning. All four were married men and quite innocent of any connexion whatever with the Partisans. But last night's attack that had begun in the small hours of the morning had developed and been driven home. Two policemen had been killed and another wounded.

At first, picking out the four unfortunates seemingly at random the Germans had decided to try them summarily and then shoot them out of hand. Vasil Kumovich, in his capacity of a member of the "Shutz-Politzei" into which he had been reluctantly pressed, had interposed on his countrymen's behalf, with the result that for the moment they had been spared.

"But the Germans have said to my father," said Luba, "that if there is the least trouble — any attempt to escape or any demonstrations from the rest of us outside in the village, that the prisoners will be shot immediately and there will be another one, policeman or no, to be shot as well and first of all, and that is my father."

"One day," said Walter, who had returned late from Radzimichy, "this will all be over. One day we shall be left in peace to live our lives in our way. Even misery doesn't last for ever —"

Luba jumped to her feet and stamped her foot again but this time it was not to get rid of the snow.

"When that day comes," she said, "where shall we all be? And which of us will be alive? Have we ever been free? What happened at Zastarynnio six weeks ago? I was there, taking a can of hot soup for my father who was on duty. But those others — the police — were there first. My father and I stood and watched. They fired the tracer bullets into the thatch and into the wooden walls. Soon the whole of Zastarynnio was on fire. Men and women ran out of the houses, there were old men and women amongst them, and young girls with babies in their arms. They ran out of the houses screaming and then the Germans fired upon them with their machine-guns. They fell as they stood or as they ran. There were great pools of blood and I saw a little child with both arms blown away lying face down in the snow —"

"Ah, no!" said Sasha tenderly. "You are beside yourself, Luba. Let me take you home."

"I can find my own way," she said. "It is all very well for you Sasha Nioman with a sister and brothers around you, to share all your troubles. It's different for me."

Walter found Luba's cloak and wrap and put it round her. It was Walter who took Luba home on his way back to Radzimichy, where he was now staying in the schoolhouse. Sasha crept off miserably to bed.

Though he lay over on his side when Nicola came into the bedroom and pretended to be asleep, sleep was out of the question. He was hurt and unhappy because Luba had rounded on him so unjustly. He had meant no harm nor implied any rebuke. It was only the truth which he had spoken; everyone was overwrought to breaking point. As for himself only what passed after midnight would tell.

He tossed and turned in his bed till Nicola began to snore. He could, Sasha told himself, wake Nicola and confide in him, tell him of Ivan's discovery, of his dreadful threat. He longed to do so. Nicola, who was strong and certainly Ivan's match would thrash Ivan, but would that mean an end to the matter? Ivan would still have a tongue in his head.

There was but one solution to this fearful problem; to admit to Ivan that he had a gun in his possession, to go to the wood and find it and together with the ammunition hand it over. Only that way would Ivan's lips be sealed, and the family secure.

And after that Ivan would go off with his friend to join the Partisans, because that was only too clearly his intention, and so there would be an end to this menace of Ivan, who might even be killed fighting for his new friends, which would be the very best solution of all.

A quarter of an hour after midnight there was a movement outside the window.

Sasha, tense and alert, saw the wavering light of a torch across the window-pane. Then the darkness swept in. Before the signal could be repeated Sasha was out of bed. It would be an hour later tonight before the moon was fully up.

Sasha left his bed and crossed the room. He was fully-dressed. He had put his clothes on an hour before, after making sure that Nicola still slept soundly on. He passed through the living-room and round the huge tiled stove where the wood embers glowed redly in the darkness through the chinks of the iron hinges of the oven and tiptoed to the front door and opened it. It had stopped snowing.

He passed over the threshold, closed the door gently behind him and made his way round to the back of the house. He could see a dark figure outside his bedroom window. As he stepped silently forward across the snow, the torchlight went on again, its beam directed into the room. It was, Sasha decided, the third flash of the signal. He was furious with Ivan for his clumsiness in lighting up the interior, it was enough to wake Nicola and then indeed the fat would be in the fire. But he was glad he had made up his mind to give the rifle freely. Very soon now it would all be over and a mighty weight lifted from his mind. He would never behave in so foolhardy a fashion again. He took another step forward.

"Ivan!" he whispered.

The torchlight immediately went out.

"Ivan Zavada," he whispered again. "It is Sasha. I will take you up to the wood Ivan. The snow will have covered everything, but no doubt —"

There was nobody by the window. At first he could not be sure, because the light from the torch had made it difficult to see in the dark, but in a few seconds he was quite certain of the fact. The figure had melted into the darkness. There was nobody there.

"Ivan," he whispered a little louder.

There was no reply. In the utter silence of a snowbound world where a regiment could have marched soundlessly he thought that he heard the faintest of clicks. Sudden fear ran down his spine like a trickle of icy water. He stared into the darkness, peering, listening.

"Where are you, Ivan?" he said through lips that were as dry as paper.

There was no answer. Instead, there seemed to be a movement, an envelopment all about him. There was a shambling of dark figures closing in. He gasped and held out a wavering protesting hand. He began to back away, to retreat from this imponderable, sinister pressure in front and around him. It was like the up-surge of a dark and rising tide.

Immediately behind him, as with hand outstretched he groped his way backwards to the familiar wooden walls of his home, he heard a smothered cough. A second later he felt the cold muzzle of a pistol pressed hard against the nape of his neck.

He stood stock still. The night all around seemed peopled by the legions of the damned. He could hear their breathing, and now accustomed to the dark, he could see the glint and glitter of a dozen eyes. All seemed focused upon him. He could feel the panic bubbling in his throat. He heard through the window the scratch of a match. Then the light of a kerosene lamp suddenly glowed from the inside of his bedroom.

Nicola must have heard something. Nicola was awake. The light from the lamp fell through the window, a golden pool on the trampled stow. It fell on the frosted head of a tall man in a belted sheepskin jerkin with a cheese-cutter cap perched jauntily at the side of his head, who stood between Sasha and the wall of the house. It fell on the short squat figure of a woman with the flattened nose of the Mongol and heavy lidded, unblinking eyes holding a revolver against the nape of Sasha's neck. She wore a scarf tied round her head. She looked like a witch. On the edge of the golden pool stood seven other figures of men, belted and heavily armed, with automatic rifles at the ready.

"Take us round to the door in the front, little brother," said the woman in an undertone. "You should know the way." She spat into the snow.

From the inside came Nicola's voice:

"Sasha... where are you... where have you got to...?" Inside the bedroom the light wheeled across the ceiling. The golden pool in the snow took on the shape of an ellipse. The man with the cheese-cutter cap swung Sasha round by the arm.

"Don't you know what it is to obey an order?" he said. "Lead the way."

4

There were seven of them altogether including the woman. There was no sign of either sledges or horses. Out of the dark night they had arisen, determined and dangerous. Another had ranged alongside the leader taking Sasha's forearms in an armlock. The leader's pistol was now prodding at his back in the region of his kidneys.

"There must be no tricks," whispered a hoarse voice in his ear. Of course there would be no tricks, with one stripling, weaponless, against nine armed desperadoes.

Sasha laid his hand on the front-door latch and it lifted silently. Then they were all but one, who remained on guard outside, crowding behind him into his home. He heard the faint metallic rattle of the bolt as someone slipped it into place. These were persons accustomed to the needs of their desperate business which brooked no bungling. Each was trained to his position in a team itself, in turn, trained for death, each knew what to do swiftly, accurately, expertly.

"Light up," said the voice.

In the confined darkness of the house the air was heavy with breathing, rank with the sour smell of the unclean. Sleeping rough in the woods in winter clothing was not conducive to any niceties of the toilet. The hand on Sasha's forearm released its grip, but there was still a point of pressure in the small of his back. He groped in his pocket, found the matches which he sought, struck one. In the wavering, ragged flame he saw momentarily the heavy lidded eyes of the woman in a face that looked leaden and dead. Then he was fumbling for the table and the kerosene lamp upon it. Seconds later the room was lit.

The leader motioned with his hand. The team took up their posts, two on either side of the room which Sasha shared with Nicola, another two before Papa's bedroom and the one remaining drew the curtains. There was movement by now inside both of the two rooms; the door of Papa's suddenly opened.

He stood in his pyjamas, blinking and winking at the light. Then he started back, but one of the intruders had already crossed the threshold and as Papa stumbled an iron-tipped boot heel pinned him by a toe as neatly as a nail through a bare foot, to the wooden floor-boards. His mouth opened with a sudden spasm of pain, like a little black hole in the middle of his sleep-mottled face. The man on his other side was rocking on his heels, puking drunk. A stolen Luger sagged from his right hand.

"Where is the pig you killed today?" said the leader.

"I killed no pig," said Papa.

"You are a liar," said the drunken man.

He spat in Papa's face and lurched against him as Papa wiped the spittle from his chin. Then he grabbed Papa by the shoulder and swung his arm back.

"Why do you lie? I saw you. I was watching. Do you think we are fools to leave a trail back to our camp when we can lie up in your woods all night and watch."

"Stand aside, Stiopa," said the leader irritably. "Let the fellow get his boots on. Stand away. We don't want any more accidents like the one with the boy last night — with you and your drunken guns."

He motioned towards the woman.

"The clothes and blankets, Natasza. See what you can find."

He turned again to Papa.

"Get your boots on, and lead us to where you keep the pig."

Sasha, standing unmolested now by the leader's side, saw Papa's eyes upon him and the dawning look of astonishment and scorn upon his father's face.

"Did my own son open the door of our home to you?" he said, and his voice was thick as if he was in liquor. And then to Sasha:

"Why are you in your outdoor clothes?"

"To hell with your son and his clothes," said the leader as the other bedroom door opened and Nicola emerged. "Get your boots on," repeated the leader to Papa.

Nicola was half-dressed in shirt and trousers. There was no astonishment upon his face. There was no reason to be surprised. It had to his way of thinking been only the luck of the draw that had occasioned the delay of such an overdue visit. Now he was glancing questioningly from his father to his brother and then back again, and his eyes were bright with curiosity at the remark he had overheard. The woman Natasza was pushing past Nicola into the room beyond, jabbing at his ribs with the muzzle of a tommy-gun to impress him with the urgency of her mission.

The drunken man called Stiopa staggered from Papa's side and crossed to Nicola.

"I know you," he said.

Nicola shook his head.

"We have never met before," he replied.

"What liars you all are," said Stiopa. "First the old man and now you."

Papa moved into the bedroom and picked up the ankle-boots that stood together at the foot of the bed. He began to pull them on cursing under his breath. Three armed men stood over him, their weapons levelled. One was hissing impatiently as he waited. Papa looked over his shoulder where his jacket and breeches lay on a chair, and made as if to reach towards them.

"That will do," said the Partisan nearest to him. "A breath of fresh air and a nip of cold will clear your head and smarten your brain."

They pulled Papa to his feet and between them with the loose pyjama jacket unbuttoned round his throat he led them towards the front door. As they opened it with the leader at their heels, Sasha could see the figure of the guardian outside wheeling round, his automatic rifle at the ready to cover any eventuality. If on the previous night at Petroff's place the boy Sergei had lost his head and attempted escape, it was now clearly understandable how an "accident" had occurred.

The party of five passed down the path towards the barn and the sties. The moon was up but haloed with the misty warning of another snowfall and the air was softer than the night before, when the flames had licked round the timbers of Petroff's house. Two empty sledges had mysteriously appeared in the road beyond the gate. The drivers stood at the horses' heads.

Papa made his way to the barn. When he flung the double doors open everyone could see the splendid shape of the newly killed pig, scrubbed pink and white, hanging from the shining steel hook from the beam above.

"Take it down and carry it to the sledge," said the leader.

It seemed that it was not sufficient to deprive a household of its precious food without resorting to insults to its owner. Two of them helped Papa unhook the carcase and straddle it head-down with a leg apiece across each shoulder but it was as much as Papa could carry, strong as he was, and he stumbled at the first step. Someone muttered: "Pick up your feet, old Rusty-Guts," and that raised a smothered laugh which the leader sternly repressed. Then staggering and lurching Papa progressed down his own garden path and reached the first of the sledges. He slung the pig across the runners and then, with neither a look to left or right, and with his head bowed as if there was a great weight still between his shoulders, he plodded back through the trampled snow towards the barn.

The party had moved towards the sties and three of them had entered and were turning the sow out of her stall. Papa at that outrage broke into a shuffling run and began to cry out.

"No, no!" cried Papa. "Not to kill the sow. She is in early farrow. All of us need food, Germans and Partisans and Byelorussians. We are all men. We must all live. Kill the sow and we lose our food. We die."

"Who said any German was fit to live?" said the leader. "I'm of a mind you 'play a tune to suit the German flute'. We need another pig."

He made a gesture towards the men in the sty. One of them stepped forward drawing a pistol from the holster on his belt.

"For pity's sake," said Papa. "For the love of God, leave the sow." He stretched out his hands as if to take the leader by his shoulders, by his arms in supplication, but the leader struck Papa's outstretched fingers aside with a blow from the barrel of his tommy-gun which set Papa clasping his agonized knuckles between his knees.

"Another move from you," said the leader, "And the sow won't be the only thing dead in her sty."

Inside the house Stiopa had driven back Nicola step by step as he had retreated into his room, backing away from the threatening gestures of the drunken man who now kept an uneasy half-hesitant forefinger on the trigger of his pistol which wavered in his victim's direction. Sasha, helpless and aghast at the spectacle, knew that at any moment the crashing report of a shot would be followed by the sight of his brother collapsing across the bed where he had now been forced into a sitting position. And meanwhile for all the world like a busy housewife engaged upon her lawful occasions the woman Natasza, her little pig eyes bright with greed and desire beneath their hooded lids, stumped and strode from kitchen to larder, from cupboard to shelf, choosing here an enamel plate or two for her own use in camp, there a shirt or blanket or more, and all the time the very walls resounded to Stiopa's exhortations and accusations.

"You are in the pay of the German Field Police... You are one of them."

"I am not. I don't know any of them."

"Another lie. Who is Vasil Kumovich? You would not know the pretty Luba with the red ribbon in her hair? Ho! ho! That has him there! Deny it, deny it if you dare!"

"That is true. Vasil Kumovich is my cousin and Luba is his daughter, but that doesn't make me an informer or a spy."

"Those who are not with us are against us. Either you are a patriot and a Partisan or you are a traitor and deserve death."

"Leave him alone," said Sasha, unable to contain himself longer nor further endure the suspense of watching that twitching forefinger on a metal trigger.

Stiopa swung round and the pistol traversed the length of Sasha's figure.

"You keep your mouth shut, little rat," said Stiopa. "And anyway with whom did you have an assignation tonight when we came on the scene? Was it a tryst with the pretty Luba at dead of night?"

"No one," lied Sasha, and turned aside knowing that despite the distraction of the present appalling situation, Nicola's questioning, tortured eyes were full upon him.

"If you," said Stiopa, turning back to Nicola, "would like to think your family will still have a roof over their heads by the morning — if indeed you should wish me to plead their cause with our leader that they should be spared — well, you have but to prove yourself."

"How do I prove myself," said Nicola, "When you are determined not to believe a word I say?"

"We are always glad of recruits," said Stiopa, with a chuckle.

Nicola rose from his bed. He drew himself up and it seemed to Sasha that the tall young man had never seemed so tall and straight nor his shoulders so square for all the pallor of his face and the inadvertent trembling of his lips.

"Is that your bargain?" said Nicola.

"Call it what you like," said Stiopa, suddenly savage again with the liquor within him on the turn. "What do I care? If your heart's not in the right place — Bah! What is one more dead man among so many dead already?"

He levelled his pistol at Nicola's chest. Nicola stood utterly still. It seemed to Sasha, tense and watching, that in this supreme moment his brother was turned to stone for there was now no movement at all upon his face which seemed to shine with the exaltation of a saint, and though there was something like a taut steel wire stretched to breaking point and twanging within his own brain, he was fully conscious that he was witnessing something which in all the years to come and whatever they might hold, would be indelibly recorded on his memory, and that this was indeed the way a man should face death however foolish and unjustifiable that end might be.

And then from the direction of the barn came the sudden sound of a shot. Three more shots followed and then there was silence.

At the sound of the first shot, his purpose as suddenly forgotten as it had been conceived, Stiopa spun on his heel and staggered across to the door where the sentry still waited. They began to talk together in low tones.

Nicola was taking his jacket from the row of hooks above his bed. His hand was shaking now that his moment had passed, and the perspiration was rolling down his cheeks. With dread in his heart Sasha watched him cross to the chest of drawers which they shared and take an assortment of underclothes which he laid upon the bed. Then as if he were moving in a dream unaware of his own actions he began to pack, filling a kit-bag which he took from beneath the bed, folding each article carefully and neatly.

"What are you doing?" said Sasha desperately. "What are you going to do, Nicola?"

Nicola shrugged and continued to pack. It was almost as if the full significance of Sasha's question had failed to penetrate the trance which enveloped him.

Out in the living-room the woman Natasza was sorting out the loot she had collected. Beyond, a little way down the path, Stiopa and the sentry still talked earnestly together. There appeared to be some movement in the distance by the barn, a trampling to and fro and men whispering discreetly.

"Who have they shot?" said Sasha. "Nicola, Nicola, you heard the shots... Who have they shot?"

"I don't know," said Nicola.

"There could only be one person," said Sasha. "Why are you packing, Nicola? What does it mean? I didn't mean to let them in, Nicola. You know that, don't you? I wouldn't let them into my own house on purpose, whatever side they were on. I didn't go to meet them. If Papa thought that... and now if the shooting... Oh! Nicola, Nicola, *you* don't believe I let them in!"

"I don't know," said Nicola again in the same flat voice.

"I didn't. I didn't," said Sasha despairingly. "Why are you packing? Don't leave me, Nicola. Don't leave me alone. There isn't anybody else I can go to. I didn't dare go to Papa and tell him about Ivan Zavada."

"Ivan Zavada," said Nicola dully. "What's he got to do with anything … I don't know what you're talking about …"

"Papa would have been so angry …"

Sasha moved swiftly to Nicola's side. He caught him by the sleeve of the sheepskin jerkin which he had just put on. Nicola said nothing, but he brushed Sasha's hand off his arm as if it had been a horsefly that had settled there. There was movement all about the house by now, and the subdued sounds of muttered orders and counter-orders. There seemed to be some sort of human chain from the steps of the house, down the short garden path and into the road where the two sledges waited with the patient, champing horses. The pillaged property from the Nioman household was being passed along the line, blankets, clothes, utensils, food and lastly the swollen massive sow with four shots in her head, dragged on a sheet of corrugated iron across the trodden snow.

But in the room which they had shared for so great a time Sasha stood blinking his dismay at Nicola; looking first in his brother's direction and then down at his own hand as if he were still finding it incredible that Nicola should have scorned his touch.

A sudden anger filled him:

"Well, if you won't believe me you can go to the Devil!" cried Sasha beside himself.

Nicola made no reply, but he picked up the kit-bag and slung it across his shoulder. Then he went down the steps of the front door as Papa began to cross the yard by the barn. Nicola was by the garden gate as the Partisans began to clamber aboard their laden sledges.

"Wait for me," said Nicola. "I'm coming with you."

"Good, my brave fellow, that's what I like to hear." It was Stiopa's voice and it sounded very friendly.

"There's more room on the other sledge," said the leader. And then to the drivers:

"All right. Off you go!"

In a very few minutes there was no sound, not even that of a faint, distant drumming of galloping hooves.

Papa passed into the house. There was still light in every room. Sasha was kneeling by the great stove in the centre of the hall, attempting to raise a glow in the embers with the hand-bellows. Valia, her hair tied in little knotted rags, stood nearby in her nightdress. She was crying softly, helplessly to herself. As Papa came in Sasha dropped the bellows, with surprise and relief.

"The shots!" he said. "We heard shots …"

"They shot the sow," said Papa curtly. "Where's Nicola?"

Sasha shook his head. He wanted to tell Papa everything that had passed between him and his brother and of how there hadn't been time to say anything properly; not time indeed to say something which now might never be said. Instead he himself could scarcely speak, because there was a terrible constriction in his throat. He beckoned Valia to him and she came at once. Still kneeling he put his arms around her strong, slight body.

"You should have slept on, little sister, and not let them wake you. I will take you back to bed."

But when he tried to rise the effort seemed to become too great, so that he clung to her, clasping her to him fiercely with all the passion of his grief and despair. So they remained while

Papa lit another lamp and placed it on the living-room table, which was always a sign that he was distraught, and was going to sit up for the rest of the night with at least one litre of vodka to help him through.

5

How could he live on without Nicola? Again and again he asked himself the question, sitting by Valia's bed where she now at last lay sleeping. He had put out the light in the room but he still waited lest bad dreams should come to her and she awoke. She had cried herself to sleep. Through the half-open door leading to the living room he could just see the end of the table and a glass on the corner. It was a painted glass with crude, brightly coloured flowers, and was the only one that remained of half a dozen which Mamma had bought in Radzimichy at the time of the summer fair two years before her death.

He had watched Papa's hand come into the circle of light cast by the second lamp on the table and tilt the vodka bottle thrice in the last hour. So it would go on till dawn and if one bottle ran out there was always another. Quite soon now Papa's chin would drop down towards his chest and his mouth would gape and then he would begin to snore. Sasha was glad Papa was out of sight round the post of the door. He was not an edifying spectacle in his cups.

What should he do without Nicola? Many a time Nicola, as the older brother, in days past had stood between Papa and the others when a quarrel had been imminent, in just the same way Mamma when alive had protected her children. As for himself after Mamma's death he had turned to Nicola for many needs and consolations. It was Nicola who had explained why when the Poles had occupied their country he had not been able to go on to college. The Poles were Roman Catholics and under the Pilsudski regime which began in 1920 no Byelorussian could attend college unless he changed his religion. Once Pilsudski had driven in full uniform and glittering medals and silver braid through the little country town of Radzimichy on his way to take a review in Baranovici. Sasha and Nicola had stood by the kerb hand in hand and Mamma had kept a hold on their shoulders. Sasha had felt the clasp of her fingers suddenly tighten and had looked up at her. It had shocked him to see the snarl upon her gentle lips. Pilsudski's car had been passing and he was raising his hand in stiff salute to the peak of his General's cap. It had seemed to Sasha at the time that Pilsudski with his tremendous moustache was making a great to-do about very little. Though the streets were lined with Byelorussians no one had been cheering, except a few Poles who were present.

It was Nicola who had told him of the origin of the Byelorussians; how three centuries ago they had been a proud and independent race, just as the Latvians and the Estonians, the Lithuanians and Ukrainians, the first three with their northern borders on the Baltic: it was Nicola who could draw maps with intriguing coloured chalks showing how before the First World War there had been no Poland which had been under the Czarist regime and shared a border with Germany, and how, during and after the First World War her independence had been recognized. Moreover Nicola had a knack of collecting tales about the various races which from time to time had overrun and occupied Byelorussia; tales like the ones that always seemed to arise from the various cemeteries scattered round the countryside and which roused Sasha's sense of the romantic since some were the graves of Napoleon's French soldiers on their tremendous retreat from burning Moscow, and others were the records of men who had fallen in another war 1914–1918. Besides it seemed to give

Nicola a certain malicious satisfaction in recounting the occasions when Byelorussians had been overrun.

For himself he could remember the Poles only, and later, when in 1939 Germany had attacked Poland and that unhappy country had been shared out with Russia, the Russians had come in. Then the Russians had been driven out when the Germans broke their treaty and attacked them and so the Germans had arrived; and because the Germans had taken the Russians' place, Russian Partisans had come into being, while at the same time there were Byelorussians serving in the German Field Police whose task was to keep the Partisans down. And now Nicola was a Partisan, not of his own choosing, but because caught in a cleft stick he could save his family in no other way.

And now what was to happen to him? Would the occasion ever arise when he would be able to explain all that had happened on this hideous night? Would he ever be able to approach Papa, when he'd sobered up, and lay his troubles before him? No, never in the same way as he could have done with Nicola. At the mere mention of a rifle concealed on his property Papa would fly into a fearful, unreasonable rage. Yet in the end he would probably have to go to Papa because sooner or later that young brute Ivan Zavada would come round with his loutish threats.

Sasha went to the window and drew the curtains. Dawn was creeping into the freezing sky and a few flakes of snow were beginning to fall. There was an ugly tinge of dull red in the low cloud-wrack above. It seemed to stain the whiteness with its own sombre colour. From where he stood he could see the outline of the barn and the trampled slush round the pigsty. Then he saw that there was a trail of blood from the sty, across the yard, travelling towards the garden path where the raiders had dragged the newly-killed and still bleeding pig towards their sledges. Even the snow was stained with blood, red and crimson as the little wicked flames which had flickered round Petroff's barn and house only the night before, flames which could eat and destroy their own house, the one he now stood in and which Papa had first built for poor dead Mamma for her marriage gift. All around on every side they were beset with blood and ruin and disaster. It was more than a human soul could stand.

He dropped on his knees by the window sill, and began to whisper:

"Dear God, please send Nicola back to me …" And then in tones almost of panic: "I don't know what to do … I don't know what to do."

He dug his nails into his knuckles in the intensity of his pleading. When he rose to his feet he felt chilled through as if he had lain out in the barn half the night and the cold had stiffened his joints. The dawn was fully risen and the colour had gone from the clouds. The sky, like the snow and the world around, looked grey and squalid.

From next door sounded the steady unhurried murmur of Papa's snoring.

6

At ten o'clock of the following morning Ivan Zavada called. He was self-assured, jaunty, and banged on the door as if he owned the place, calling loudly for Sasha. It was quite evident that he not only expected to receive what he had come for but that he was confident that he was in possession of Sasha's secret with all the additional power over another human soul which gives so much pleasure to a bully.

Sasha opened the door at once. There had been a fresh fall of snow and most of the traces of the night's marauders had been obliterated. Nevertheless the sight of Ivan standing with one foot on the top step almost as it were half-way over the threshold was distressing. Compared with the other troubles which beset Sasha the threat of Ivan had momentarily faded into the background. Now on the instant his persecution loomed up again formidable and menacing.

"I couldn't keep last night's appointment," said Ivan affably. "The heavy snow that fell yesterday damaged the roof of my barn. Several of the timbers came down with the weight. It took me all the afternoon and half the night to repair it. However, I'm here now."

"Yes," said Sasha. "I see you are."

A spirit less mean would have noticed the strain on the young hollow-eyed features and taken pity, but that was not Ivan's way since he knew no better.

"Well," he said. "Have you got it ready for me?"

"No," said Sasha.

He was scared of Ivan but his hatred of him and his kind was still greater. It seemed to have grown keener overnight for some reason.

Ivan, accustomed to have his own way appeared for the moment disconcerted with so blunt a reply, but he was swift to recover himself.

"Our little cock-bird is preening his feathers early this morning," he said. "I suppose that comes of having visitors last night. Was it a pleasant party?"

Sasha was very white, even his lips looked bloodless and there was a hooded, grey look on his face and that long-sighted intensity of focus deep within the eyes that only pain, either physical or mental, can bring.

"They haven't plundered your home yet, Ivan Zavada," said Sasha, "otherwise you wouldn't talk like that."

"They've more sense," said Ivan. "Now have you got what I've called for?"

"No," said Sasha. "I haven't such a thing in my possession."

"You're a liar," said Ivan evenly. "And what's worse a bad liar. I've heard the shots, haven't I, as I told you before. And what was it you had in your hands just before I came up with you in your wood the day before yesterday?"

"Well, if I could find what you wanted, Ivan Zavada, would you go away and not come back?"

It was a painful thing to have to say, but only too clearly Ivan had seen and heard too much. The repetition of the facts drove the force of them home.

"I should only come back perhaps sometimes for more ammunition," said Ivan and chuckled to himself for the witty fellow he could be. Then his mood changed.

"Enough of this fooling," he said harshly. "I've had enough of it. Get what I want and hand it over."

"It isn't here," said Sasha desperately. "I swear before God that it isn't here."

"You were to have it ready for me last night," said Ivan. "So it must be."

"I threw it away," said Sasha. "When I saw you coming that morning I threw it away."

"Do you expect me to believe that?" said Ivan. "What's got into your mind? You know what I've threatened to do if you don't deliver the goods. I shan't hesitate."

"Give me time, Ivan. I've got to have time —"

"I'm tired of this nonsense," said Ivan. "Where's your father? Maybe he'll have more sense."

"He's sleeping," said Sasha.

"Oh! He is, is he?" said Ivan. "Well, we'll soon see about that."

Without another word he pushed past Sasha into the living-room. Sasha followed speechless at his heels. There was no use in arguing with a creature of this calibre. There was no humanity nor mercy in him. He only knew what he wanted and nothing would deter him. In a ruthless world, he too was utterly ruthless. Very well then, Ivan should have his rifle and that should be an end of it all. He would go up to the wood and find it, and though the capitulation was very bitter, it was the only way out of this monstrous situation.

"Give me a little more time, Ivan," said Sasha. "You shall have what you want. I promise it."

"I've had enough of your promises," said Ivan.

He crossed the room and flung open the kitchen door. Valia, peeling potatoes at the sink, turned at his violent entry and, startled, dropped the knife she held, clattering. The sudden look of renewed terror on her face was another stab of pain to

Sasha. Then Ivan turned on his heel and was across the room and at Papa's door. He passed inside.

One glance at the figure, still in its day clothes, sprawled on the bed was sufficient, but Ivan strode to the bedside and seized Papa by the shoulder and shook him. Papa grunted in his deep stupor and rolled over on his side. Ivan muttered an oath and turned to face Sasha.

"Where's Nicola?" he demanded. "I'll get some sense out of him." Sasha stood silent as Ivan repeated his question. Despite himself he was trembling. There seemed that there could be no end to this long agony of fear that fed upon itself and bred still further fear.

"Where's your brother? Where's Nicola?" said Ivan.

There were no words to meet this question. There must be words which could convince, but Sasha couldn't find them. Even if they had come to him he doubted if he could speak coherently. He could hear himself stammering some wild excuses. He was telling Ivan that Nicola had gone to the farrier to have the pony shod and Ivan shouting back that he had passed by the forge on his way and seen no one waiting and that the forge itself was barred and shuttered and that Sasha was lying again. He himself knew that he was lying now, outrageously, but he was fast losing his head and his grip upon himself. It was all getting too much, the terrible night, and then this equally terrifying visit of Ivan's. All around him, on every side there was trouble and disaster.

"Ah!" said Ivan, with sudden triumph. "Now I see it. Nicola isn't here because he's gone away. So that's it, is it? They took Nicola with them as well, last night!"

He did not wait for an answer.

"Well, I am going back home. I shall be in my barn, finishing that job. But if you do not come within two hours and bring what I want with you — well, you know the consequences. I shall go to the German Headquarters and tell the officer that not only has Sasha Nioman been concealing firearms, *but that his brother joined the Partisans last night!*" And with that Ivan Zavada stormed out of the house.

It would be all right Sasha kept on telling himself, as if the repetition would lead to conviction. Everything would be all right. The great thing to do was to keep calm, to keep very calm. Just now he had nearly lost his head but now with Ivan gone he was feeling almost himself again. All he had to do was to go up to the wood and fetch the rifle and take it along to Ivan. He was glad that he had resolved to contend with Ivan no longer. It was humiliating to give in, but there was no other course open. The family could stand no further suffering.

He crossed the yard to the barn where he kept his skis, found them and put them on. There was no real necessity to take skis because he could reach Ivan's place by the road running through Dubrova village. The surface of the snow on the road would be trampled firm and the going would be good. Nevertheless once he had secured the rifle he could take a short cut across the fields from the wood at the back of their own home to the back of Ivan's house. Moreover it would be safer that way. However much he disguised the rifle with wrappings there could still be a chance of encountering a passing patrol or even a single member of the German Field Police and then there could be awkward questions with disastrous results. Besides speed was an element in this situation which, thank God, he had at last solved. He had two hours in which to act and he would travel faster on skis, and once the hill to the wood was mounted and the second hill between on the way to Ivan's house climbed, the land fell in a fine downward slope to the valley in the crook of whose arm the village lay.

Therefore he put on his skis and with his pockets stuffed with paper and old canvas to conceal the rifle, he set out on his brief journey.

There had been two heavy snowfalls since he had last been in the wood. The fence on the right of the copse originally crowned with a drift was now completely submerged. The white surface continued uninterrupted from field to field as if there had never been any intervening division. In the wood itself only the larger clumps of thicket and thorn showed above the wind-rumpled surface.

It was, Sasha judged, just to the left of the big fir tree with the broken bough that the fox-earth lay. Once he had rediscovered the earth he would be able to re-orientate his position in which he had been discovered by Ivan on that fatal morning and from which he had flung the rifle into the thicket which had opened its arms to receive it.

He was sufficient of a practical countryman bred and born to realize the difficulties which faced him but he had little doubt of achieving his object. It was, he reiterated to himself, merely just a matter of orientating from point to point once he had pin-pointed the fox-earth. Then he noticed that the lower branch of another tree a few paces to his right was also broken. This was a trifle annoying because it made the initial step in the logical sequence open to some doubt. It could mean for instance that the last step, which would lead to the thicket into which the rifle had fallen, could be to the left and to the right. As such a conclusion could be diametrically opposed, then the distance between two such points would be doubled. The thing to do then was to make quite sure that he began correctly.

He took stock of the two trees standing half a dozen paces apart amongst others of their kind. They were approximately the same height and bulk for bulk of a similar shape. But the broken boughs differed. One, over-weighted by snow, had been wrenched half off by the wind near the trunk, the other had snapped in the middle and hung by a green-stick splintering. He chose the former, because he was certain that his instinctive judgement was the better and began to scour the surface of the snow with his ski-stick.

It was surprising how after only a couple of days and amidst familiar surroundings the aspect of a countryside could change. The well known outlines of the small hills and gentle valleys were clearly discernible, but it was when the less ostentatious landmarks came to be considered that the disparities became more evident. Indeed the smaller the object the greater the differences in appearance after one heavy fall followed another. In the extreme example any well known characteristic could obviously completely disappear.

The ski-stick was not the best of implements with which to make such a search. He up-ended it, hoping to collect on the point of the wooden butt some sample of the soil beneath. He remembered that the ground round the fox-earth had been heavy with yellowish clay. When he pressed down into the snow the ski-stick encountered branches and obstructions, but nothing with the solidity of bare ground. The second fall of snow had been heavier than he had imagined.

Perspiration broke out on his forehead and he told himself that it was pretty hard work probing about in thickets under the snow. In fact it was very considerable hard work and that was what made a fellow sweat. People were known to sweat from anxiety of course — "break out in a sweat", was the term

— but that could scarcely apply to the present situation — or could it?

The thought occurred to him as he caught sight of the other tree with the green-stick splintering. The fibres of exposed wood were dark and grey. With fear in his heart, scarcely daring to raise his eyes, he glanced at the breakage of the bough on the tree he had first chosen. The fibres, several of which had actually snapped and stood out from the remainder, were pale and yellow.

The branch of the tree on his right had been broken before the branch of the tree on his left. On the day of Ivan's intervention there had only been one broken bough. He had been searching under the wrong tree. This time then there was no need to diagnose the causes of perspiration. He glanced at his watch. It was half past ten.

But there was no occasion, he told himself, to panic. The rifle couldn't be far away. If the worst came to the worst, he would tell Ivan Zavada precisely where the wretched thing was hidden; he would explain that it had originally been concealed in the fox-hole and that once that had been found the rest was easy, because it would only be necessary to go forward step by step. Even if Ivan had to wait till the spring, the rifle would still be there.

He was getting confused in the head again. Ivan didn't want to wait the better part of four months for the rifle. He wanted it now, within two hours, and that wasn't correct either. It wasn't two hours, it was now, with this dreadful loss of time only a hour and a half. He began to jab and probe frantically between the two trees, till the ground was trampled and confused and several times when inadvertently he stood upon a submerged thicket it gave way beneath him and he fell waist deep in a tangle of thorn. At the end of another half hour he knew that the rifle could never possibly be found in time. It was hopelessly mislaid. It was close at hand, but for all it meant as far as he was concerned it could have been at the bottom of the deepest pit in the Baltic.

The hot wave of fear swept through him again. It was like drowning in a sea of terror. If only Nicola were here a solution could be found. Nicola would have unravelled this dreadful tangle. The minutes were mounting up and Ivan would be waiting in his barn in the village below.

What a fool he had been, thought Sasha, to have imagined this latest problem of so little consequence, and yet it could have been so easily solved. Chance could have taken a hand and led him in the first instance to the right tree, because the rifle was there all right, almost as it were, within a hand's grasp. It almost destroyed faith in God, thinking that way. God could so easily have ordained it otherwise, had He so wished. And that was wrong wandering up that heretic path, letting doubts creep in where conviction should rule. Nicola wouldn't have approved.

But what in Heaven's name was he to do? All the evil forces of all the world seemed to be combining against him. Wherever he turned to find a fresh trail through the maze, that trail was blocked. When he retraced his paces he became confused and lost afresh; then when he thought he had found his way again another obstacle suddenly arose and forced him to retreat once more. So this whole baffling process repeated itself, unfolding itself within itself in bewildering circles, ceaselessly, endlessly.

It was no good waiting where he now stood, torturing himself, scourging himself in exasperation of frustration. Time was flying. He must do something, move fast. It was madness standing here wringing his hands and stamping his feet. But where could he go for help? If the rifle wasn't in Ivan's possession within an hour and a quarter at the most then Ivan would be in the police commandant's office laying an information.

There was no doubt that Ivan would abide by his threat. In this tortured land overrun and depopulated, populated afresh by another source and overrun once more, there was nothing in the least unusual in neighbour deliberately betraying neighbour. That indeed was a commonplace only to be equalled by the deliberate "planting" by one rival faction against another, of prohibited articles such as firearms in barns, outhouses and attics and for which the penalty was immediate death without trial. Whichever party or nationality was temporarily in power it was taken for granted that its members would seek vengeance for past retributions from their former rivals; an appalling, timeless, ceaseless, repetitive, vile cycle that had chased its own tail for miserable centuries of war, murder and rapine.

Papa was the right and proper person to approach. He was the head of the family — or all that was left of it. Only what would Papa say or even more drastically what might he do? It was several years now — Sasha had been a mere schoolboy at the time and not a fully fledged young blood of sixteen and a half summers! — since Papa had laid a strap across his bottom. That was scarcely an eventuality; even if Papa got rough he would stand up for himself. He would tolerate no indignities. He could retaliate. It was only this confusing sequence of intolerable events that bewildered him, like fighting a way through a wall of fog and cotton-wool, instead of tearing down even with his bare hands the granite battlements of an inscrutable fate.

Well, since Papa had by now probably come to his senses, he should be consulted in this hour of need. Leaving the wood, though it cost him a pang to forgo one last maddened search, Sasha swept down the short slope to the house.

Papa was more or less himself. He was standing before the mirror in his bedroom surveying his crumpled, creased clothes, and his swollen face and heavy eyes, while he fingered the point of his bristly chin with a spatulate yet distasteful finger. His debauch had done him no good nor eased his temper. As Sasha came in, he caught sight of him in the glass and growled:

"No sign of Nicola?"

With his heart leaping within him Sasha said:

"No! But should there be?"

"Not at all," said Papa. "Only sometimes they break away — change their minds. Oh! I don't know. Is there no end to all this?" Adding, "What do you want?"

"I've something to tell you, Papa," said Sasha. "Something to confess. I'm very worried …"

"God in Heaven," said Papa, "Aren't we all worried? Don't you think I've got enough on my shoulders with two pigs and a son missing, without you to come to me with your schoolboy troubles?"

"They are not schoolboy troubles, Papa. They are very serious —"

"So was everything when I was your age," said Papa. "When you're a grown man you'll think differently. It's time you made up your own mind over little problems, and not come worrying me, as if you were missing your mother's apron strings. One day you'll have to make decisions for yourself. I don't see why you shouldn't start now."

"Very well," said Sasha and his usually pale cheeks had a little red patch by the cheek bones which often appeared when his pride had been touched and he was vexed. "Very well. From now on I'll make my own decisions. But I'm going to tell you what I came to tell you about whether you like it or not."

At that Papa turned from the looking-glass and smiled. He smiled into Sasha's eyes which were level with his own and he laid a hand on Sasha's shoulder.

"Go on, son," he said. "I don't mean to be severe with you, but we've been born in hard times and it's not been for the asking of you and me for all we've had to put up with and for all we've both lost. Go on, tell me your troubles."

"I have been hiding a rifle," said Sasha. "It was in the wood up on the hill … in a fox's earth … And Ivan Zavada found out … and last night I was to have met him but he didn't turn up … but the Partisans found me waiting by the window... that was why I was dressed … I didn't lead them in … Nicola's gone and I hadn't the time to tell him what had happened... God knows what he's still thinking... and now there's only about an hour to go and Ivan is waiting for the rifle and I can't find it…"

"You should have told me before," said Papa, not unkindly. "Get a spade and we'll go up to the wood and have another look. But I don't think it's any good."

Hope rose again within Sasha's heart because though the time was getting very short he knew now that Papa was on his side, nor had he upbraided him. They went up to the wood on the knoll together and very soon the snow was scored and trampled and stained with spadefuls of black and yellow soil and clay, but there was no sign of the rifle.

Papa leant upon the spade and mopped his forehead and shook his head.

"No good till the spring," he said, adding with some bitterness, "And I don't suppose your friend Ivan Zavada is prepared to wait till then!"

But there was a sudden light in Sasha's eyes. Something of his customary buoyancy had returned though Papa looked glum, wondering no doubt to what other use and for what other purpose his spade might soon be put.

"Last night," said Sasha, "Nicola went with the Partisans, but he never joined them as a volunteer. He felt he had to go to save his family. Otherwise they would have burnt our house down over our heads. Very likely the Germans will come soon and question us about last night, and then if they learn about Nicola's going — if Ivan has told them about that as well as the rifle, we shall suffer again."

"I have little doubt of that," said Papa grimly.

"I've been the cause of a lot of trouble," said Sasha. "I didn't mean to be but that's the way it's worked out. But Nicola saved the house and family from the Partisans by joining them, so why can't I save the family from the Germans?"

"If you can think of a way," said Papa, "you'll have me astonished. But if you've a suggestion you might as well make it while we wait here for the clock to tick our lives away."

"Yes," said Sasha. "I have an idea. We were spared by the Partisans because Nicola joined them. Maybe we'll be spared by the Germans when they arrive if I've joined the German Field Police — first."

"Join the Germans?" said Papa as if he had not heard aright. "You to join the Germans!"

"Like the hundreds of others of us," said Sasha. "Only I shall have a better reason than they. If I am forced to fight against my own countrymen I have an excuse. The Germans won't punish you and the family if I'm already one of them. That is if they will accept me before Ivan Zavada tells them what he knows. Is that a good scheme, Papa?"

Papa stood silent for several seconds, leaning on his spade and seemingly studying the ground by his feet. He kicked a clod of earth across the snow before he lifted his head and his eyes were troubled.

"It would not be for myself..." he began. He seemed to behaving some difficulty in formulating his thoughts. "But there is Valia .... and the other boy ... though Walter is not here for the moment he could be traced within a few hours... not for myself, I swear it ..."

He shook his head and shoulders like a dog emerging from water and shaking itself dry. It was as if he were throwing off the bad thoughts and worries from him, rousing himself from his half-nightmares which chased each other round and round in his mind and never got anywhere. Sasha laid his hand on his father's arm.

"The idea could work," he said eagerly.

"You must make your own decision," said Papa. "I cannot influence you. You must decide for yourself."

"I will go into Radzimichy right away," said Sasha. "And I will find out what the chances are. The Germans need recruits just a much as the Partisans. We shall see, what we shall see."

"I will go down to Ivan Zavada's house," said Papa, "And ask him how the roof of his barn is going on and how he repaired it, because my roof too has been weakened by the snow. I shall keep Ivan in conversation as long as I can, till you have a good start ... Good luck to you, my son."

That was clearly Papa's way of giving his consent without committing himself. Sasha dug his ski-sticks into the crisp snow-surface and glided off.

It would be just over one kilometre and a half to Haradischa as the crow flew, over the open country, and there was just time to complete the journey before Ivan began to get worried. There were no clearly conceived plans in Sasha's head but he was little concerned on that score because the town would be full of Germans and he could make enquiries of the first he saw.

He made his way slowly up the gentle slope whose crest was crowned with the German Military Cemetery of the First World War. Often as a small child he had visited the place after he had learnt what it was and wondered why it should have got there. Now he knew. He skirted the graveyard wall with the drifted snow level with its exterior and noticed how the wooden crosses were covered up to their cross-pieces and the stone memorial in the centre up to the top of its plinth. It confirmed his view that it had clearly blown harder than he had imagined on that second night of the snowfall and it was understandable how the branches of the wood where the rifle still lay had been broken. But that was small comfort now.

Nevertheless the more he considered his plan the more feasible it appeared to be. It was perfectly true, as he had told Papa, that the Germans needed recruits for the Field Police, whose task was to keep the lines of communication open and undamaged from the raids and sabotage of the Communist Partisans who operated vigorously all over the range of occupied country that lay between the German front line and the German bases. The Field Police were officered by Wehrmacht commissioned and non-commissioned officers and their ranks were filled with others like himself, volunteers from Byelorussia, the Ukraine, Latvia, Estonia and Lithuania.

He reached the end of the cemetery wall where the ground fell away in a long, steady decline towards the last valley before reaching Radzimichy, when he could take to the road. As he began to run down the valley-side he glanced at his watch. He had still three quarters of an hour in hand but time was still pressing though Papa would minutes ago have reached Ivan's house.

Sasha always took pleasure in ski-ing. It was an accepted form of locomotion in the winter, but he invariably found it exhilarating. Now as he sped down the valley-side with the keen air in his face and the drumming of the wind in his ears his mercurial spirits rose again. He urged himself forward zestfully. The plan was bound to succeed.

The road to Radzimichy lay to the right and he could see where it ran almost parallel to the little tree-fringed River Servach beyond. Here and there were isolated homesteads along the roadside. He gained speed as he reached the mid-slopes and swung slightly right towards the distant town. The last hill before Radzimichy began to rise before him as he struck the hidden snag.

It could have been a log, a fallen tree, a boulder, even another fox-earth. Whatever it was it was concealed. The urgency that inspired Sasha may have made him less observant than was his custom, but the force with which he struck the unseen, concealed obstacle, threw him for the moment off his balance and into the air. He landed with the point of his right ski deeply imbedded in the snow. As he pitched forward on his face his ski-sticks flying from their wrist-straps, the ski snapped off short at his toe.

He got to his feet again and surveyed the damage. This was not the first time that such an accident had occurred — it could indeed happen to anyone — and he knew that it was in itself trivial. It merely meant that his further progress would become a kind of dot-and-carry-one dragging his left foot out of the snow, propelling himself forward with his ski-sticks on one leg till the impetus ceased, and then beginning the whole slightly ridiculous process all over again. On downward slopes fair progress could be made, up hill the climb would be laborious.

But it was completely exasperating that such an accident should have occurred at a time like this. He glanced at his watch again. There was half an hour left, if Ivan prompted by his vicious temper chose to set out for Radzimichy on the first moment of the time limit he had declared. That Papa might delay the start was more than doubtful if Ivan's mind was set upon it. Rather it might aggravate the situation since it would be with a malicious sense of the sardonic that one like Ivan would contemplate the presence of yet another of the family involved in the whole squalid and deadly business which he himself had in hand. But now whatever might be taking place in Ivan's barn one necessity remained — to press on with all speed.

The snow was softer than was customary at this time of year. There had been fewer degrees of frost on the previous night than were to be expected. Every time Sasha's left leg touched the surface it went in well above the knee. He had fallen at the bottom of the valley and as he toiled up the slope before him, his progress became increasingly slow. Half way up, pausing for breath and leaning on his ski-sticks, he found himself gazing to the right. His attention was concentrated on nothing more than regaining his breath. Then he realized that he was intent on the distant figure of a man walking at a smart pace along the road. There was something reminiscent of Ivan Zavada about the figure, tall and lithe with swinging arms.

The sight set Sasha scrambling up the slope with a burst of renewed energy. It was a waste of effort for by the time he had reached the crest he was momentarily exhausted and must rest again. The figure below, silhouetted dark against the white background, was swinging steadily along the road confidently and determinedly.

For that distance it was impossible to identify who it might be but Sasha's suspicions were fully aroused. It looked like Ivan and it could be Ivan. On the other hand it might very well be a complete stranger. But so great was the strain and tension to which Sasha had been subjected that he became convinced that his enemy was on his heels. He started off down the last slope before Radzimichy with fear in his heart. But when he reached the road and crossed the bridge over the Servach and entered the outskirts of the town there was no sign of his fellow traveller.

He came into the town by the road that led south-west to Baranovici. The Catholic church and the police station lay on his right and across the corner of the square he could see the barracks occupied by the 34th Battalion Field Police. There were armoured cars drawn up opposite and farther down the street stood an observation post and a concrete pill-box. The relief crews were manning the machine-guns as Sasha made his way past the school buildings. German soldiers awaiting parade stood in groups by another derelict machinegun nest in the process of demolition.

This headquarters had been the objective of the attack when Sergei Petroff had died and two Germans had been killed. Now where once the sheep and cattle had been driven, moving leisurely and slowly, their silly simple heads wagging or bobbing from side to side, lowing and bleating as they trotted to the market place with the drovers calling their cattle-cries behind the flock and herd; where once the tinker and the wandering men and women with their dark faces and thick greasy hair had set up their stalls and chanted their pavement wares, and where the wild-looking horsemen had cantered, caparisoned and jangling into the town; here now, there was all the grim impedimenta of war, of steel motor vehicles and the protruding metal snouts of guns. A young Wehrmacht officer was coming down the same side of the street as Sasha. He too was little more than a boy with a fair, flushed face and a little golden moustache upon his upper lip, and bright blue eyes. As they drew level with each other Sasha halted, clicked his heels together, and since he was bare-headed, stood at attention only knowing from hearsay the correct method of such salutation.

"May I have a word with you, sir?" said Sasha.

The little Lieutenant stopped in his stride, and one eyebrow went into a neat little quiz such as he had seen the Herr Hauptmann do who wore a monocle, both feats which the Lieutenant admired, and one of which he had learned to copy.

"What can I do for you?" he said.

There was a movement across the street where the school buildings were occupied by a half-company of the S.S. There was a lorry drawn up before the entrance and a dozen youths, all Byelorussians, were being urged towards it by the German guards. One tripped as he stepped across the gutter and a boot on the backside helped him to his feet. The others clambered over the tail-flap and squatted on the floor. All carried parcels or small bags containing what remained of their belongings. Sasha knew who they where and what was the nature of this other business. These were the victims of the German press-gang, daily at work pressing the local young men into forced-labour for Germany. This lorry would be bound for East Prussia. Should he himself fail to be accepted for the Field Police here was an alternative which could offer no protection for his family and nothing but calamity for himself. Already one of the guards was looking across the street in Sasha's direction, apprising him, with a watchful eye.

"What can I do for you, my man?" said the little Lieutenant with a chill in his voice. Wehrmacht officers expected immediate replies from young strangers who were clearly country-bumpkins and allowed their attention to wander.

"I want to join the Field Police Battalion in Radzimichy, sir," said Sasha. "If you could help me I should be very much obliged."

The little Lieutenant looked Sasha up and down with what he hoped was the proper critical military air. He tried to effect a little insolence but the effort only brought more pink to his cheeks, and he felt that a monocle was lacking. And as the seconds passed standing stiffly at attention, Sasha could see over the Lieutenant's shoulder the German guard, his party now all aboard, with his hand at the lorry tail-board; and he seemed to be hesitating before he raised and fastened it in place lest a transaction which he was watching across the street might fail to materialize, and there might be yet another passenger for Germany from which there could be no return.

The little Lieutenant flicked his wrist over to see the face of his watch and to impress upon the enquirer the importance of his own affairs.

"Very well, then," he said. "I just have time. Come with me."

They went down the street side by side, till the Lieutenant quickened his pace a little to differentiate the difference between a Wehrmacht commissioned officer and a little runt of a farmer's boy however bright his face might be. Sasha slowed down a little, being an intelligent young man and sizing up a situation which was only too transparent; particularly as he considered the officer to be little more than a young jackanapes and as vain as a jackdaw who had learnt to chatter.

In this way then, the one striding a little ahead of the other, but both stepping out in a brisk manner which well befitted them, they came to a handsome stone house, painted white and which Sasha knew of old, since the dentist of Radzimichy had lived here before the property had been requisitioned as administrative offices by the Germans.

They entered the house and stopped by a half-open door with "Major Holm" inscribed upon it. A guard at the door sprang to attention.

"Can I see the Commandant?" said the young Lieutenant.

The guard knocked at the door. A voice called "Come in." The Lieutenant went inside. There was a passage of indistinguishable words. Waiting in the corridor Sasha's mind reverted to the memory of that sinister figure swinging along the road as he himself had descended the last slope towards the town. It could still have been Ivan Zavada. Even now he could be at police headquarters which were nearby, lodging an information. There could have been persons in the police station who had observed his own entrance into the town. He would have been particularly conspicuous with a broken ski. If that were so and Ivan was telling his damning story, would they send round to this very office and tell this Major Holm that the application of the new recruit waiting outside his door should be disregarded? Furthermore would they demand that he should be immediately handed over for interrogation? Then there would follow the dreadful hours of question and answer with no sleep and the blazing light held before his eyes. They could even send for members of the Gestapo from their headquarters at Minsk. There could be no end of it all, as there could be no end to his own self-torturing fantasies. Then he was aware that the little Lieutenant was beside him and was saying: "Go in. The Major will see you."

Sasha went in. Major Holm, seated at his desk, was engaged in lighting a fresh cigarette from the butt of its predecessor. His hair was elegantly combed into greying wings at the sides and slightly perfumed. Then he raised his head and reclined in his chair with an arm flung over the back and a forefinger of his free hand stroking his silky moustache, while the smoke from his drooping cigarette deepened the hue of his already stained fingers. Sasha still standing rigidly at attention could only feel very unimportant indeed in the presence of this magnificent and scented personage. He hoped he had not carried a trail of snow into the Commandant's office because the Major was eyeing his snow-clotted trousers with faint disdain.

"You wish to volunteer for the Field Police Battalion?"

"If you please, sir."

The Major sighed and leaning towards a tray on the desk, extracted a form. "Do you think you would make a good soldier?"

"I'd do my best, sir."

"Let me see your identification document."

Sasha handed over his identification paper with its photo, fingerprints and name and address. The Commandant copied the details on to the form before him. Then he pressed a bell at his side. A door on the right opened and a junior officer came in. He gave the outstretched, semi-horizontal arm salute of the Storm Troopers. There was an exchange of words in German. The salute was repeated. The younger officer turned on his heel, jerked his head towards the door leading to the passage and Sasha followed him out. They were walking briskly along the street before Sasha realized they were out of the building. When they reached the square he saw that the lorry with its occupants was gone. There was still no sign of Ivan Zavada.

A Ukrainian sergeant stood at the playground gates of the school which was occupied as quarters for No. 1 Company of the 34th Battalion, Field Police. The German officer handed Sasha over. He was already beginning to feel that as an individual he had ceased to exist. Moreover, it was disconcerting to have no knowledge of the German language. While the officer and sergeant conversed briefly together, a feeling of intense isolation passed over him. It was as if he had suffered a sudden bereavement. Then he was alone with the sergeant and aware that he was being addressed in his own tongue.

"I am Sergeant Schiller. How are you? What are you joining us for? Do you want to be killed by the Partisans? You are very young."

He was gay, pleasant and inconsequential. Sasha felt more at ease.

"I am sixteen and a half years," said Sasha.

"A mere baby," said Sergeant Schiller. "Does your mother know you're out?" It was an old saying, but Sasha hadn't heard it before. He wasn't sure that he liked it.

"My mother died three years ago," said Sasha.

Sergeant Schiller sucked at his lips sympathetically.

"Too bad," he said. "Now come with me and we'll see what the Field Police can do with you."

There was a palliasse on the floor and two blankets in the class room to which Sergeant Schiller led Sasha. There were also some forty other members of No. 1 Company in the room, some lying on their filled mattresses, others squatting on their blankets, others standing or on their knees cleaning their rifles and automatic weapons.

"You will sleep here. This is your bed," said Sergeant Schiller. "You will parade with the others for dinner in half an hour." He grinned and patted Sasha on the back. "Make yourself at home," he said. "It's not so bad when you get used to it. Never say 'die.' See you later!"

"No," said Sasha. "Never say 'die'."

He was beginning to like Sergeant Schiller.

The group in the corner nearest Sasha were talking about him. He couldn't hear what they were saying but they kept looking towards him. He supposed because they were older men that they always took the rise out of people younger than themselves who were newcomers. If Nicola was here he would know what to say to them. Nicola would have had none of their nonsense. He wondered where Nicola had spent the night — up in some wild and windy encampment no doubt, amidst the trees and thickets of a dark and desolate wood. Nicola was a Partisan now and he too would have to learn a new way of life. He wouldn't have had a palliasse filled with straw — he'd be lucky if he had a blanket, unless they'd given him one of his own, one they had stolen from Papa's house! Maybe Papa was back from Ivan's place now. He wondered what might have happened. Even now none of them were safe. Then he remembered that in his panic haste he had not even said goodbye to Valia. She would be wondering where he'd gone and begin to pester Papa with questions, and Papa himself worried beyond all measure would be short with her and there would be more tears.

It was nothing but tears; tears and blood and hopeless misery, a constant striving for an existence which was little more than a dog could snatch out of a garbage heap. Courage and goodwill didn't seem to matter, but courage and decency did matter because Mamma had always said so and Papa had constantly confirmed her views. Mamma must have been right, because Nicola had always followed her principles and at times had even reminded Papa of them. But Mamma was dead and Nicola was gone. He himself hadn't even said goodbye to Valia nor touched Papa's hand in farewell. And now he was alone in a great bare class-room that was being used for a barrack room, full of strange rough fellows who were laughing at him. He could hear them laughing at him. He was alone and all the world was against him. He could feel the hot tears pricking at his eyelids.

Then of a sudden the full impact of the situation struck him like a knuckle blow in the teeth. He was a member of the German Field Police. He had clearly been accepted. He had even been allotted a bed. Soon no doubt they would give him a uniform. But the duty of the Field Police was to hunt down Partisans. Nicola was a Partisan.

Realization of this tremendous fact swept all else out of his head. One day he and Nicola could meet face to face, and the life of either of them would depend on who fired first. Somebody was laughing and making coarse jokes about girls, and if the mother's darling who had newly joined had had a woman yet. They were talking about him again but he didn't care. All he could see was Nicola's reproachful, doubting eyes on the night of the raid; all he could hear was Nicola's toneless voice, "I don't know."

He turned as a fierce-looking man with a scar running across his cheek jostled against him.

"Out of my way," said Scar-face and winked across at his companions. "Who are you pushing about?"

"You, of course!" said Sasha, with some of his former spirit, and neatly dodged the cuff across the head that was aimed at him. Everyone laughed at the sally and the discomfiture of Scar-face and the laughter was of a kinder note.

Nevertheless he was glad when it was time for dinner. A corporal had already brought him one of those combined spoons and fork and a billy-can. He joined the others in the playground outside and lined up with them; then it was "left turn, quick march" into the kitchen where a ladle-and-a-half-full of stewed meat, cabbage and potatoes went into the billy-can. He carried it back to his bedside and started to eat. Nobody took any notice of him as they spluttered and sucked and chewed at their food. When it was over they belched and loosened their belts and sprawled upon their beds. Snow was beginning to fall again and the wind was rising. Somewhere in the recesses of the building a door began to bang intermittently, maddeningly. He felt better after his meal and cleaned out his billy-can and washed his spoon and fork at a sink in company with the others. But when he returned to the class-room, the dark mood of depression and loneliness began once more. The pangs of home-sickness were upon him.

At mid-afternoon, when the sky was purple-black and the snowflakes were getting larger every minute and his depression deeper, another corporal came for him. He was told to follow and went across the playground once again and past the kitchen, towards another block of buildings, with double swing-doors in the middle. They passed through and turned into a small room with bare shelves running along three walls. It could once have been a library. Again the floor was covered with palliasses and blankets, and there were some forty young men cleaning their equipment and rifles. It seemed a permanent occupation of No. 1 Company of the 34th Battalion Field Police, when the weather was unfavourable. A group of them stood together in a corner of the room.

"This is your platoon," said the corporal. "These will be the chaps you work with."

He allocated a bed to Sasha and left him. Sasha laid the billy-can and spoon and fork carefully on the top blanket. It was the first piece of military equipment with which he had ever been issued. He felt rather proud of it. He began to wonder when they would give him a rifle. He was quite a fair shot having practised at dusk near a wood not so very far away. Then the memory of that same rifle, now lying lost beneath the snow, came flooding back with all its miserable associations.

"Sasha Nioman," a voice called. "What are you doing here, Sasha?" It was a familiar voice. He looked up. It was Mikita Tomko who had been in his class at the elementary school in Haradischa, just behind the Greek Orthodox Church. He had grown inches since Sasha had last seen him, and his shoulders were broad. He was standing in the corner surrounded by a group of other men of like age. Mikita was eighteen.

"Come and join us, Sasha Nioman. And glad I am to see you." Mikita thrust his way through the group and took Sasha by the hand. By the side of the big young man Sasha looked like a foal beside its sire. Mikita put his arm across Sasha's shoulder and guided him into the circle.

"Andrei, Symon... Alles... this is my old friend Sasha... We were at school together... Such a little rascal. No mischief too much for him, none too small. These are my friends, Sasha Nioman ... my friends of Number One Platoon of Number One Company ... the smartest of them all... Come closer, Sasha, we have something here."

They were passing round some object from hand to hand, standing in their tight little circle, elbow to elbow. The bottle found its way into Sasha's hand.

"Drink up," said Mikita's hoarse whisper in his ear. "Drink up. It is forbidden by the officers but that only makes it taste the sweeter."

The laughter gurgled in his throat.

"To hell with all Partisan bandits," said Mikita and seized the bottle for his own turn. The vodka was burning in Sasha's throat.

"You're in the Army now, Sasha Nioman," said Mikita. "It's a great life. To hell with all bandits. Never say 'die'."

"Never say 'die'," Sasha repeated.

It was astonishing what a friendly word could do. At the moment life seemed much worth living.

PART TWO: YOU'RE IN THE ARMY NOW …

1

The first shot from the wood on the left of the road set the horse which Sasha held rearing. It was on its hind legs pawing frantically at the air with its forelegs, while Sasha hung on to the halter with all his might. He was among the first of the halted column and the horse was young and frightened. The wood lay just over half a mile ahead where the road began to swing to the left before it entered the village of Masty six miles north of Radzimichy.

At first there were only half a dozen single shots when the screen of scouts of No. 2 Company reached the belt of trees that lay black against the waste of snow, but it was sufficient to set the entire force leaping from their sledges and deploying into line on either side. Then the machine-guns started.

There was a man detailed to every horse of the thirty sledges on the company's establishment and a "kutscher" for every company officer; each "kutscher" joined his fellows as they hurriedly selected suitable cover and flung themselves down, controlling their charges with the long rope of their halters. It was impossible for Sasha to take cover for he needs must keep on his feet to hold close to the bit. Only too easily, as he well knew, could the bit be loosened from the mouth of a restive horse and the bridle slipped free. Because of that kind of knowledge they had made him a "kutscher."

They were opening a steady fire now on the wood ahead and it was being returned with intermittent bursts from the Partisans who had hoped for an ambush. That hope had not been fulfilled but the action was warm.

Nobody seemed to know how many Partisans were likely to be engaged nor for that matter their total number within the whole area. But a report that Partisans had been seen had come into headquarters at Radzimichy from one of the spotter aircraft — old "crates" — that trundled through the sky at a hundred miles an hour. When the information was passed on to Minsk the order promptly and curtly came back to destroy whatever enemy forces there might be, forthwith.

The whole battalion had moved immediately. Three of the companies were developing their own encircling movements over three areas south and south-east of Lake Switaz, but No. 1 Company had been allocated the district nearer home.

There was heavier fire from the wood ahead. Every now and again Sasha could hear the thud and "plop" of a bullet striking, and an uneasy whining whistle through the air. The horse was the platoon commander Lieutenant Kubik's and it was Sasha's duty to hold the horse when his officer went into action. He could see the lieutenant at this very moment, ducking down behind a withy patch and slipping in the soft snow.

In Sasha's opinion the lieutenant wasn't a bad old stick, being nearer forty five than twenty, as were all the German officers and sergeants manning the battalion with their Byelorussian and Ukrainian counterparts of equivalent rank, both up and down the scale. On the other hand it was probably Kubik's fault that the horse was not properly trained in so much that he had no eye for horseflesh. This judgment Sasha had reached after one week and a day with the Field Police and he still had no uniform.

The lack of a uniform and the fact that he was only a "kutscher" was humiliating. A "kutscher" was only a glorified stable-hand; he looked after the horse, fed and watered it, bedded it down and groomed it. He carried no weapon of any kind, wore his civilian clothes and seemed to have no status, certainly not as a fighting man. All during this first week of his service in the Field Police Sasha had inwardly railed at his task. If he had volunteered as a soldier, at least they could let him fight. But whatever his views might be on that subject he was at the moment under fire for the first time in his life and was pretty certain that he was not in any way looking upon the ordeal with favour.

Every time a machine-gun chattered, the horse sprang sideways or flung itself once more on its heels. It was a powerful beast and it dragged Sasha across the road so that he slithered into the snow-filled ditch. He slid down and went up to his knees in water. It was still February but the weather was beginning to break.

He clung on to the halter and the horse's head went down as he slipped so that he brought the animal to its knees, and its snorting, distended nostrils blew hot in his face. They scrambled up together, skidding and slithering, and somebody nearby — just audible over a burst of automatic weapon fire — seemed to be yelling directions. Sasha thought they could go on yelling for eternity for all he cared. They could have the job of controlling this fear-maddened brute if they thought they could do it better than he could — to hell with them all.

He clung panting and perspiring to the halter. The horse's withers were white with sweat where the rope had chafed and it was trembling and twitching all over. At another burst of fire it began to back violently away, dragging Sasha with it.

"Let the bloody thing go," said someone lying in the snow before rising to his hands and knees preparatory to making a dash forward.

There was fully a section up by the wood by now engaging the Partisans at almost point-blank range. At the very last moment the Partisans would break off the fight, darting and diving through the trees, and after a parting burst of fire would disappear. So it would go on till the enemy like mackerel in a seine net would be encircled. Often enough the fish escaped before the net was closed.

"Get down under cover," said the speaker. "You'll get yourself bloody well shot."

It was Mikita Tomko giving advice. On either side of him individual members of his platoon were dashing forward in short rushes. The old-fashioned sectional rushes with a whole *Gruppe* dashing forward at a time had long since been abandoned with the tremendously increased fire-power of modern automatic weapons.

"It's the officer's horse," said Sasha panting.

There were little white puffs in the snow where the Partisan bullets skimmed the surface. Out on the left flank but not very far away a man doubled up clutching at his belly with both hands, his rifle spinning from him. Then he fell on his knees and the snow was stained crimson. He pitched forward on his face as Mitika rose to his feet and began to run on.

They had brought up the half-battery of 45 millimetre anti-tank guns and by now were beginning to shell the wood. The horse, exhausted by its own terror, stood shivering and shaking.

The brief battle was receding into the distance as the company advanced and the Partisans broke cover. The anti-tank guns, after two or three rounds ceased fire. Soon it would be time to move on up with the sledges and horses to where the company held its new position. Then when the scouts had gone on again, fanning out ahead, and when it was safe to advance, everyone would clamber into the sledges or form up in the single-file infantry marching formation on either side of the road and the advance would continue, until another sudden volley heralded the next hold-up.

The signal-whistle to bring up the horses and sledges sounded within the next ten minutes. The column moved slowly down the road. Where it began to skirt the wood Sasha could see Sergeant Karol waving them forward. Everybody said that Karol was easily the best soldier in the company, and that included all the commissioned officers, except the commander. Mikita Tomko and his friends thought the world of Karol. He was half-Pole, half-German and had been trained by the regular Wehrmacht. Aged thirty, he was dark and smooth-mannered, with a bright brown eye. He never found any necessity to raise his voice to get things done. Sasha had no personal knowledge of him. Somehow he thought with that soft manner and cynical twist to his thin mouth, he might be an awkward customer to offend in any way. But not so very different after all from Major Shaeffer who was in command, tall and fair with his hair going grey at the sides. He was a German and a splendid officer and very fair and just to every man under him; so everyone said at any rate and there ought to be something in the opinion coming, as it did, from such a mixed bunch as the legionnaires were composed of, being Ukrainians Byelorussians, with a goodly smattering of Lithuanians, Estonians and Latvians.

Sergeant Karol was still by the side of the road when Sasha came up with the horse and Lieutenant Kubik had joined him. Kubik was getting too old for this kind of fighting. It was young mans stuff and demanded too much from a middle-aged man who had himself been through the First World War and in this one had lost two sons; one before Maastricht on the Western Front and one in the Luftwaffe, bombing Coventry. Moreover the R.A.F. had destroyed his home in Berlin and killed his wife. It didn't seem that Lieutenant Kubik had much encouragement to continue living, but as little Paval Kaluta who was one of Mikita's admirers, had remarked, that nobody knew what went on in a fellow's mind when he reached that age. Probably senile decay had already set in.

The lieutenant and the sergeant were talking earnestly together when Sasha approached. The scouts had already gone on ahead with one complete section to clear the nearby valley.

Sasha took a piece of rag from a bundle which contained his clean kit off the leading sledge as it moved past, and led his charge to the roadside where he could wipe the sweat from the chafed withers and clean off some of the slush and muck which had mingled with the snow and was clotted and high on the flanks. If a "kutscher" was all they thought he was fit for, then at least he'd make a job of it. When he had finished, he urged the horse into a trot.

As he drew nearer to the officer and Sergeant Karol he heard his own name mentioned. He had no idea why he should have been of any interest to either of them being a mere menial but he was intrigued to see Mikita Tomko hurrying towards the two men as if he had been suddenly summoned. The horse had quietened and was showing less of the white of its eyes. Sasha wondered if he himself revealed any outward signs of fear. He hoped not, although it had been very unpleasant with the bullets whistling past as he had struggled with his charge; and it had all happened so suddenly, the slow progress along the lonely country road, and then the crack of the shots and everyone scrambling off their sledges. Maybe, they had all been too busy with their own affairs to trouble about him, but he had been horribly afraid and he could perfectly understand Mikita's injunction to look after his own skin. As he drew level with the little group of three, he realized for all his inexperience, that something was wrong.

Mikita was standing to attention. His automatic-rifle was slung on his shoulder but his free finger tips were stiffened to where the seams of his trousers should be. His face was very red, and had that set expression of pursed lips and unfocused stare common to all private soldiers of all nationalities, when receiving a rebuke or avoiding an awkward question.

Sasha halted with the horse and waited. Sergeant Karol was doing the talking.

"Well," he said to Mikita. "Did you or didn't you? Haven't you a tongue in your head?"

The tip of Mikita's tongue crept out and he moistened his lips.

"Well?" repeated Sergeant Karol.

"Here's the boy himself," said Lieutenant Kubik. "Ask him." He was one of the few Wehrmacht officers who spoke Polish.

Sergeant Karol looked Mikita over contemptuously. Then he turned in Sasha's direction and his bright brown eyes with the little gold flecks in them under the steel-helmet were lively with intelligence and quick wit.

"Did this man tell you to desert your post and leave the officer's horse?" he said.

So that was it, thought Sasha. He hadn't been in the army for the better part of a week without knowing the answer to that one. If the sergeant was going to describe the act of a ten-a-penny "kutscher" letting go of his charge when under fire for the first time as "deserting his post," then Mikita could be in serious trouble.

"No," said Sasha stoutly.

"No?" said Sergeant Karol incredulously. "But I was within earshot."

As the commander of the second platoon he would have been on Mikita's flank, but it had all been too confusing and bewildering to remember.

"I heard nothing," said Sasha.

"But I was there. Didn't you see me? Did or didn't this man shout to you to leave the horse and take cover otherwise you'd get yourself killed?"

"I never heard him," said Sasha stoutly.

"Oh! let it be," said Lieutenant Kubik. "It doesn't matter. The horse is safe."

"Very well, Sir," said Sergeant Karol and turned on his heel.

"Get back to your work," said Lieutenant Kubik to Mikita, adding: "And watch that tongue of yours in future."

He mounted and rode off down the road. Sasha clambered into the sledge and Mikita trudged along beside him.

"Very well done, little rascal," said Mikita. "You saved my skin all right. That Kubik, he is an old fool. I don't think much of these German officers. They are not front line troops. Now that Sergeant Karol, he is a different proposition."

"I don't know much of him," said Sasha.

"How should you? You have only been with us a week."

"As a 'kutscher'," said Sasha bitterly.

"Well, what of it? You are very young —"

"I came to fight," said Sasha. "Isn't that what you are here for? And when the war is over and Germany has won and Communism is finished with, we shall get our reward and they will make Byelorussia a free state — and we shall be a free nation."

"You know all about it," said Mikita, grinning.

They were passing through the wood by now and the tall trees on either side of the road where laden with snow though their tops were bare and dark against the afternoon sky. The column went forward slowly and painfully. It seemed to Sasha a cumbrous method of dealing with such an enemy. It was hit or miss, and all the enemy needed to force the company to halt and deploy was half a dozen shots. Then they would slip through the ring once more, the soldiers would form their column again, and the whole laborious business would continue. There were clearly no Partisans in the wood now which was rapidly thinning out, while the ground fell away to a distant village. He could see the houses clustered together and the figures of the scouts ahead approaching the first buildings on the outskirts. Within the hour they were passing through. The sky was overcast and it was growing very cold.

"I must drop back now," said Mikita, "And join the others. If you do not like being a 'kutscher' you should take my advice and see that Sergeant Karol. You look very cold, Sasha. Stop the first civilian you meet and take his overcoat."

"I'm not going to rob civilians," said Sasha.

"Pooh!" said Mikita. "When you're as old a soldier as I am you will rob anybody."

At first sight the village looked deserted. Every door appeared to be locked, every window closed. The only sign of life seemed to be several half-starved mongrels snuffing and snapping at one another round an empty garbage bin, but twice Sasha saw the furtive flicker of a curtain and once in the dusk a ghostly face at a window. News of the approaching column had preceded it and the inhabitants, men, women and children, had all gone to earth.

By half-past three the company was clear of the village, and as the screen of scouts came level with yet another wood a sudden burst of fire sent them on their faces again while the column was forced to deploy. Lieutenant Kubik cantered back down the road, dismounted and flung his reins to Sasha.

"Try and find cover," he said. "I don't want anything to happen to the horse."

The skirmish lasted half an hour, then as the darkness increased and snow began to fall both sides broke off the engagement. By the evening the company had reached a hamlet along a side road and taken over every available out-house, stable, barn, and in some cases the cottages themselves, for the night. Sasha found himself in a stable with the horse and a billy-can of luke-warm soup and potatoes. But he bedded the animal down as soon as he'd eaten and then as night fell chose a truss of straw and an empty stall for himself. He took off his boots and lay down. It was growing still colder and the stable was draughty. He burrowed his way deeper into the straw. There, two hours later, making his rounds as Duty Officer, Sergeant Karol came across him. He was carrying a lantern he had taken from his own billet. He held it above his head and surveyed Sasha in the steady beam of its light. A Ukrainian corporal accompanied him. It was comparatively warm beneath the straw and Sasha had slept. It had not been altogether an unsatisfactory kind of day. He had been under fire for the first time and had not made a fool of himself. Moreover, he had been able to repay Mikita Tomko for his friendship at their first meeting and that was a cause of considerable satisfaction. But at Sergeant Karol's entrance he woke and scrambled to his feet and began to brush the straw out of his clothes and hair.

"Ah!" said Sergeant Karol, "The 'kutscher' Nioman."

He regarded Sasha through half-closed eyes. In the golden light of the lantern with the dust-motes from the stable straw dancing in its rays, he looked very handsome with his lean, dark face and gleaming keen eyes.

"You lied to me this afternoon, didn't you?" said Sergeant Karol.

"I am sorry if I did, Sir," said Sasha.

Sergeant Karol turned to the corporal and winked his eye.

"He is sorry if he did," mimicked Sergeant Karol. "But he doesn't admit he did!"

Then he addressed Sasha again. There was a little frown on his forehead.

"What are you doing in here? Why aren't you with the rest of the platoon in the barn?"

"I am guarding the horse," said Sasha. "He's young and nervous. I daresay when I've had him a bit that I'll get him quietened down. He'll get used to me but it's not as if he were mine and I rode him. Then in a very short time I'd have him properly schooled. But it doesn't give you a chance when most of the time the officer's riding him."

"You don't think of the lieutenant's horsemanship, eh?"

Sasha shrugged a shoulder.

"It's not of much consequence if I did. I'm only a 'kutscher'."

"Well, what of that?"

"I came to be a soldier, not a farmer's boy."

"Do you think you are to be trusted with a rifle?"

"Why not, sir? I can shoot."

"If you were given a rifle," said Sergeant Karol, "should we wake up in the morning and find you and the rifle gone?"

"Gone, sir?" said Sasha. "Where should I have gone to?"

"Maybe to join your elder brother," said Sergeant Karol and he looked straight into Sasha's startled eyes. Then he jerked his head in the corporal's direction and moved towards the partitioned stable door. Both men went out.

So that was the reason they had made him a "kutscher!"

2

Mikita and two of his friends, Symon Ravin and Paval Kaluta were trudging along by the side of the sledge and they appeared to be in good spirits. It was the following morning and the company was on the move again. Paval had found a string of partially cooked sausages wedged behind a scullery copper where a terrified farmer's wife had hidden them at dusk the night before. The sausages had made a very excellent addition to a breakfast of thin gruel, black bread and ersatz coffee. The men were in good spirits and were laughing and joking and Paval, every now and again, would glance admiringly at Mikita who strode along with his chest thrown out like Thor, and little Symon in his too big boots and overlong greatcoat, plodded along with the tip of his nose blue with cold.

From time to time he would glance cautiously from under his steel helmet which he wore at all times, towards the bare open country that lay on their right flank. He was always reasonably happy when the countryside was open. It was only when it was wooded, particularly when the trees came right down to the banks and borders of the road, that he began to get the cramp in his right arm, because it was then that he kept his hand, hard and fast, on the sling of his rifle in case it should be needed quickly. Sometimes towards the end of a day's march, even if everything had been quiet, the cramp in his arm would be so bad that he knew his fingers, if an emergency should arise, would be useless on the trigger. Then he would take to changing shoulders so frequently that it had become a habit and was now fast becoming an obsession. Quite often he wondered if any of the others had developed such tricks from a prolonged and repressed fear that was slowly driving him mad.

But Sasha on the sledge sat silent with his black thoughts. So that was why he was only a "kutscher." They didn't trust him with a weapon. They had heard about Nicola and they were watching him himself lest he were preparing to play that old trick of volunteering for the Field Police in order to get a rifle and then desert to the Partisans. But if they knew all this, from whom could the information have come but from Ivan Zavada? That led to a train of more terrible thoughts. If Ivan had taken his sworn revenge, were these officers and sergeants, whom he'd been with now a week and hoped to count as his companions and brothers in arms, all playing cat-and-mouse with him, all speculating on what his next move might be, while back in Radzimichy Papa was lying with a bullet in his heart and Valia, ravaged, lay dead, while not so far away the human wolves of the Gestapo were closing in on Walter, the sole survivor of a family that was soon to be no more?

Such thoughts were intolerable and yet they had to be endured. There was absolutely nothing that could be done about a situation such as this. There was no means of getting a message through to Radzimichy and hourly he was progressing farther from home and at any moment now the bullets could start flying again and his own life blood could be spilt into the snow. As he sat behind the plodding horses he thought how utterly incomprehensible it would be to live a life where the next moment might not be the last. Somewhere, he supposed, almost out of this world, men and women lived together, ate and drank, and slept, danced and sang and had their children with never a dread thought for the morrow; somewhere — it surely could be possible and he seemed to remember having heard a rumour of it — men chose their friends because they liked them and not because they feared them, spoke their minds openly in public, careless and regardless of who might overhear; somewhere — or was that indeed Heaven where the angels played with the cherubim and seraphim and God looked on and, nodding His approval, smiled? — somewhere, where like the very sons of the bright and shining morning, men were free.

Something was happening ahead of the column. It was now approaching ten o'clock, nearly two days out from Radzimichy and a Wednesday. The day had broken with low cloud and cold, soft snow. Soon it would be the first rains of the early spring of 1944 that were falling, and the winter would at least begin to break. But here behind the German front-line, running from Leningrad, through Velikie Luki, Smolensk, west of Kiev and east of Odessa and in all that vast area between, the incessant warfare between the communist Partisans and the occupying forces was in full swing, bubbling up first here and subsiding there as the Germans took repressive measures only to emerge in another outbreak nearby. It was not unlike a great cauldron of boiling pitch with the bubbles endlessly erupting and bursting and bubbling up again and again.

Even after so short a time in the Field Police and with only forty-eight hours on his first sortie, Sasha, his fine senses quickened and alert, could tell that something was imminent. If the attempted ambush of the previous day had caught him by surprise he assured himself that it would be for the last time. The leading sledges of the column had passed by now a farm on the right with open fields on the opposite flank. Beyond, seemingly endless forest ran along a crest of higher ground. Immediately ahead lay the second village on the route of the circular tour of their offensive sweep.

Sasha knew that something was going to happen because Lieutenant Kubik had wheeled his horse and was trotting towards him, and signalling the column to halt. Already two platoons were away from the sledges and pouring out across the open ground on the left and advancing with their weapons at the ready. The "kutschers" in the rear were running to collect their charges and the detailed men were at the sledge-horses' heads and looking round for suitable cover, should the necessity arise.

Twenty yards ahead Sergeant Karol was shouting orders to the men of his platoon who were extending along the lane on the right that led to the farm.

In a short time the entire company with two platoons in advance and two in support in echelon were moving slowly towards the village and the screen of scouts were entering the outskirts moving cautiously from street corner to corner. There seemed no sign of life in the place and every window was shuttered. From where he stood awaiting Lieutenant Kubik, Sasha could see Mikita, Paval and Symon in line with Sergeant Karol's men.

Lieutenant Kubik cantered down the road and though the air was still keen there were two little rivulets of perspiration running down either side of his cheeks. He looked flustered and breathless. He himself had seen a suspicious movement amidst the low roof tops that lay ahead, and had taken it upon himself to alert the company. Somewhere farther down the road the Herr Hauptmann Fritz Weine, senior officer in command would possibly be questioning the wisdom of Kubik's decision.

The lieutenant was becoming a little tired of rebukes. He was an experienced soldier of the First World War but then his years had not lain so heavily upon him nor had loss and sorrow drained his spirit. Moreover there had been a certain stability about a war of attrition despite its muck and misery, but this jack-in-the-box caper with these damned bandits popping up in the fields, in the woods, up the trees, in any house in any village, was enough to double a man's age. Besides the former occasion when the Herr Hauptmann had thought it necessary to reprove his lieutenant he had made it quite clear, though not in so many words, that in his opinion Kubik was beginning to lose his nerve. Therefore he was in two minds as he reined up by Sasha whether to report to Weine and explain his decision and so relegate the responsibility, or to join the advance with his own platoon. The decision was made for him.

From a squat chimney-stack on the roof of a brick-built house at the first corner of the village came a sudden, shattering burst of machinegun fire. At the same time two mortars opened up from behind a broken wall and their shells exploded practically at the feet of Sergeant Karol's advancing line of men. One man fell dead immediately and another clutched at an arm which was now a spurting stump. Every man of Karol's platoon and of the rest of the extended company on the opposite side of the lane went down flat on his face. Within seconds the air was thudding and pulsating with the drumming of automatic weapons.

Kubik's mount, true to form, went up on its hind legs as the lieutenant slipped from his saddle. Then, as the latter dived for the ditch, Sasha grabbed at the halter-rope linked round the animal's neck, missed it and snatched at the off-side rein. Wild with terror the horse was on its hind legs again with Sasha hanging on close to the bit. It was like an inspired conflict between man and beast. Then, slipping on the trampled snow, the animal fell over on its side, struggling to rise with sprawling fore-legs. It flung up its head as it regained its feet. The chin-strap of the bridle snapped at the buckle. The next moment, with the bit slipping through the horse's teeth, the empty bridle was in Sasha's hands and Lieutenant Kubik's panic-stricken mount was galloping headlong down the lane towards the farm with the bullets of the Partisan cross-fire whistling over its back.

Pressed close to the ground the men of the Field Police Company were returning the enemy fire; but the maddened horse, penned in on one side by the fence bordering the line and on the other by the line of prone men, continued its wild career towards the distant farm buildings. With his head held low Sasha followed.

He ran as he had never run before and with one sole purpose in mind, to catch the lieutenant's horse before it was killed. He had no remembrance of tripping over Mikita's legs nor of hearing the infuriated shouts of Sergeant Karol to get out of "the bloody light," and take cover. The loud noises of battle were all about him. There was a humming in the air like a swarm of bees. He wondered at the time if they were bullets and how many a machine gun could spew out in a minute. He lost sight of his quarry as it dashed into the farmyard, then saw it again as it came out from behind the barn and stood hesitant and trembling. It was clear that it was trapped within the yard, unless it chose to break out by the way it had entered. It began to trot to and fro, whinnying with terror.

Sasha redoubled his efforts. He knew that he was running across the front of the defence and that the air was alive with bullets. He ran on because he knew if he stopped and lay close to the ground that he would never have the courage to get up again, nor even to lift his head from where he would attempt to protect it with his arms locked around it. He knew only two things for certain, that he still held the broken bridle in his hand, that if he could reach the protection of the farm buildings before he was hit, and if the horse didn't charge out of the yard before he reached it, that he could catch it. Therefore he ran on, with his lungs bursting and a red mist, as red as tracer-bullet trails, before his eyes.

He reached the stable yard, grabbed at the open gate and flung it shut. Then, panting and exhausted, he reached the shelter of the first outbuilding as a spatter of bullets sent a dozen tiles splintering and spinning off the roof and down into the yard. The horse shied violently from the showering debris, but Sasha made no attempt to follow it when it cantered towards the barn at the farther end of the yard. Now behind the buildings of stone and brick both horse and man were comparatively safe, and with the gate shut the capture of the animal would be merely a matter of time. Lieutenant Kubik clearly wouldn't be needing a mount for some little while; he was otherwise occupied. As for himself, he needed to recover his breath.

He had experienced no fear in his successful running of the gauntlet. It had been different yesterday struggling with that brute in the middle of the road though the occasion compared to the unholy tumult, that was now taking place had been a mere skirmish. It was, he supposed, a fact that any action concentrating on achieving a definite objective however hazardous the task, could for the moment at least, dissipate fear. He had meant to catch the horse and that was as good as done. In that there was very great satisfaction. In point of fact, he told himself, he was for the moment as the saying went, on top of the world. He was feeling, and not unjustifiably, an extremely agreeable sensation of self-esteem and elation. There was something to be said for this soldiering after all. Then, as was his way, he dropped instantly from his pinnacle into the depths. He wasn't a soldier. He hadn't even got a rifle or a uniform. He was just a "kutscher."

As always one dark mood led to another. Beyond the shelter of these protecting walls the countryside was clamorous. They must have brought up the field-guns because he could hear their bark above the crackling of rifle fire and the chattering of machine guns. It was, he thought, not at all beyond the realms of possibility that Nicola might be somewhere in this embattled village. He could fancy him kneeling at a barricaded window with his rifle thrust through a chink, squinting along the barrel, or crouching in a ditch by a mortar ready to drop in the shell, or swinging his arm back with the grenade in his fist preparatory to flinging it. Nor would it be going beyond such bounds to imagine himself, when the assault had succeeded and the Partisans had been driven out, leaving their dead and wounded behind them, discovering Nicola stretched out on his back with a bullet in his brain. Another clatter of debris and the whine and whirr of a ricochet, brought him out of his day-dreaming He must capture the horse.

For the last few minutes it had taken to trotting nervously alongside the fence by the gate. Fortunately the fence ran slant-wise back from the first of the farm buildings so that the brickwork protected the animal from any stray bullets, such as the last misdirected burst which had dislodged further tiles and part of a gutter which, torn from its bracket, was swinging like a pendulum, grating and grinding against the wall. There would be precious little chance of the farmer ever claiming any compensation for damage incurred in the fighting over his land. That made Sasha realize that at no time had he seen any movement in the dwelling-house which stood behind the farm buildings, nor a sign of cattle nor even the inevitable pig nor chickens. At the first rumour of the German offensive, those of the civil population who could afford it, he imagined, must have fled from the area.

There was no difficulty in catching the horse, now that he himself was fully recovered. He threw a rein around its neck and had the bit between its teeth and the bridle on within seconds. He was forced to leave the broken chin-strap unbuckled, but he cast off the halter rope and made it fast round his arm with a double turn.

The tumult of the miniature battle was now continuous. It seemed for the moment at any rate, that the Partisans were holding their own and that it might be some time before they could be dislodged. On the other hand the affair might go on till night and be renewed the following morning. He would be the last person, Sasha told himself, to have any views on that. He was only a "kutscher." Nevertheless he would take a look at what was happening.

Cautiously he approached the corner of the barn round which, he imagined, he could peer and obtain some sort of a view. The difficulty was the horse. He had no intention of exposing it to unnecessary danger after all the trouble he had taken. Then he saw that a secondary building, looking very much like stables adjoined the barn, and he made his way toward it. There was a door immediately opposite him and he opened it. It was a stable right enough.

This was the very thing. He would tie the horse up safely out of danger in a stall, see what was going on, and then lie up till the action was over. When everything was quiet he would return to the road where the sledges would be waiting and hand over his charge to Lieutenant Kubik. It was all quite simple, and. anyway nobody could say he hadn't done his job. He passed inside and tied the horse up at the ring-lock of a manger. He heard the cackle of chickens.

There was nothing strange in the fact that a farm should possess poultry, but it was curious that so many should be housed in such a quarter. There was a partition running from one wall to the other with a small door. He crossed and opened it.

An extraordinary spectacle greeted him. The room — there was harness hanging on its wall — was full of fowls, now on his entry in a state of great perturbation, flapping and clamouring together. In the opposite corner stood a great mound of more of their kind, but all these were dead. They formed a very considerable heap, lying with outspread motionless wings and twisted necks. There must have been at least fifty of them. Then to the right of the heap, as the remainder of the chickens escaped noisily through the open door behind him he saw the pig and the piglets. The pig, an old sow, was dead and so were the piglets. There had been a clumsy attempt to cut the sow's throat, but a bullet wound between her eyes told how she had been killed. The six piglets had all been shot. It was such a remarkable discovery, that for the time being the battle still raging outside was forgotten. What manner of farmer might this be, who kept his pigs and poultry in the same pen with the dead and living together? Moreover where might he and his family be? There had been no sign of them since the time of Sasha's arrival. His curiosity aroused, he decided to investigate.

The dwelling-house stood on the other side of the yard. There was still a great deal of noise going on in the distance but it seemed to be perceptibly receding. He deemed it safe to cross the yard and make for the house. He swiftly crossed the yard, which he noticed had been trampled by many feet and in some places bore the prints of cattle hooves in the snow. There was nothing out of the ordinary in that, but he thought it distinctly odd that he should find the front door ajar. He struck the knocker loudly twice, and receiving no reply, walked in.

He found himself in what was obviously the main living-room. There were five chairs around a table in the centre but none was occupied. On the table a meal was spread out, and there were unfinished portions of food on five plates. The knives and forks lay where they had been thrown in carelessness or — and his heart suddenly contracted at the thought — in panic.

He called out:

"Hallo, there! Hallo! Is there anybody about?"

There was no answer. In the distance the field-guns still snapped and snarled and the rifles crackled, but there was no sound within the house. He called again.

"Is anybody in? Hallo? Hallo?"

This time, in a lull of the gun-fire, he seemed to hear a faint response. It was as if somebody a very long way away was chirruping and whispering alternately. It was a penetrating, sibilant, low sound that could carry as far as a shouted word and it seemed to come from the back of the house. He opened a door and found himself in a bedroom. It was empty. He crossed to the window and looked out.

There was a vegetable garden at the back. Halfway down the snow was replaced by newly turned earth. He opened the window to see more clearly. There was a dark object crouching near a mound of soil. At first sight it looked like a sack of potatoes. It moved and he saw that the sack was the figure of a child or a small woman, its face buried in its hands. Once again the gun-fire slackened and he heard again that sibilant whispering, but now he knew it was the ghastly chattering and gibbering of one at the point of death. The last time he had heard it, unforgettable and unnerving, had been when Mamma had died. He went out by the back door and started to walk towards the sound.

He had no desire at all to walk down the garden and find what he knew he was certain to find. If the figure on the ground had been motionless he would have turned and fled, but the hands that concealed the face momentarily fell away from it. The movement betrayed that the creature still lived, but it also exposed for the briefest of moments an extraordinary, grotesque and hideous mask of a face. It looked to Sasha for all the world like that of a circus clown whom he'd last seen as a child, when all the family had visited a fair at Baranovici, long, long ago. The blotched red-and-white clown's face had haunted him in his dreams for years, as no comic creation with its distorted features and splotched red paint, but as a grinning horror. And now he was walking down a snow-covered garden path to meet this nightmare. Almost at once the hands — he saw with a shock that they too were reddened — went up again.

Paces before he drew level with the figure he saw the newly dug grave. All the way across the garden, move as slowly as he would, he had known that this was what he would find. It had drawn him on relentlessly, with a horrible fascination. He quickened his pace beyond his own volition and soon stood looking down into the shallow pit.

It was six feet long by six feet wide. There were six persons in it, in two layers of three. Those lying beneath the three above were revealed by a man's labouring boots, a woman's bare foot, a stockinged leg, a hand with crooked fingers clutching the empty air, an arm; those above were easier to discern. There was a middle-aged man in shirt sleeves, sprawled on his back. Where his breast-bone had been was a gaping wound half-a-dozen inches wide. By his side, her arm across her face as if in anticipation, to shut out the impending, ultimate obscenity, a woman lay with her knees drawn up. Next to her, almost naked but facing in the opposite direction, with her lower jaw shot away as the tommy gun had sprayed the recumbent figures with burst after burst, lay a young girl whose long, yellow hair was soaked in her own blood and that of the body beneath her. She held in her arms, clasped frenziedly to her, an infant child. The occiput had been smashed in.

Sasha felt his knees grow weak with nausea. He turned from this dreadful sight in the direction of the jibbering recumbent figure. He saw now that it must be an old woman for her hair was white.

"Oh! Grandmamma!" cried Sasha, reeling with the terror of it all. "Who has done this to you, Grandmamma? Who has done this?"

At the sound of his voice the gibbering, gave way to an intolerable whimpering.

"Who are the devils that have done this to you?" said Sasha.

The old woman seemed to become aware of his presence, through the bloody mists of death, because she took her hands down from her face and raised her head in his direction. He saw that where her eyes had been were two raw red holes, and that her cheeks and hands were clotted with congealing blood. Then her hands as before went over her face.

He dropped down beside her. The butchered family in its nameless grave, the tortured, blinded aged woman, the murdered infant and the outraged girl were objects not now of horror but of infinite pity. He knelt down in the trampled, bloodstained snow, by the mass grave with its newly turned earth, and while in the distance the rifles crackled, the mortars crashed, and the machine-guns chattered, regardless of the grime and blood, he put his arms around the old and dying woman and held her close to him. She put up a fluttering, wavering hand and her crimsoned finger-tips touched his face and stained it. She was crying very quietly to herself now, and dying very fast. Sasha held her still closer and a flake of fresh snow fell on his forehead. Soon a new fall would cover the horrors of this garden.

"Who did this to you, Grandmamma?" said Sasha and his voice was vibrant with anger.

She began to tremble and he could feel the thin bone of her shoulder as it shook beneath his hand.

"Who?" said Sasha, with all the intensity of his being. "*Who?*"

She heard and understood. The answer came so faintly that it could have been a whisper from another world.

"The Partisans." She was starting to whimper again. "The Partisans... the communists …"

Then quite suddenly her thin body stiffened, contracted. Then as suddenly it relaxed. Her hands fell from her face, her arms into her lap, her head upon Sasha's shoulder.

For a little time he waited. Then because she moved no longer he tried her pulse. She was dead. He laid her down on her side and covered her as well as he could with her shawl. The rattle and crackle of the little battle seemed to have receded into the distance.

There was nothing further he could do here, but now all that had happened was clear — the unfinished meal, the slaughtered fowls, the dead sow and piglets. What lay in the shallow grave, what lay beside it, told the story.

The raiders must have called only a few hours before the attack on the village. They had killed the fowls and pigs and collected the plunder together in the harness room preparatory to carrying it away. Then something had gone wrong. A protest? An act of defiance? An exchange of blows? It was impossible to say. What had followed he had seen for himself and would never forget. Without doubt the victims had been forced to dig their own grave, then one by one lie in it while their terrible executioners had done their work. Then they in turn had been interrupted when the first burst of machine-gun fire had set the lieutenant's horse loose. Now he would return and make certain that the horse was all right. He turned his back on the loathsome place and recrossed the yard to the stable.

The sound of the distant battle was dying down. There was no longer the clamour and exchange of fire. Now and again a shot rang out, but there was the sound of whistles more often and the occasional shout of orders. The company, he thought, were probably in possession of the village, and those of the Partisans who had not been killed were falling back to another position. He went into the stable and led out the horse. When he reached the end of the lane it was starting to snow.

There was no sign of the sledges, but down the long straight road that led to the village he could see one or two mounted men and on the outskirts skirmishers were moving. The mere fact that men were mounted could only mean the fighting was over for the time being. He set off towards them, bending his head to keep the snow out of his face. Some of it began to find its way down the neck of his lambskin jerkin. It was getting cold, and if he'd known that they weren't going to issue him with a proper uniform he'd have borrowed Papa's overcoat. But he was glad of the snow.

Very soon now the farmer's garden would be covered. No one would know, seeing that virgin whiteness, what foul shame lay beneath. As he trudged along the road his hatred of those responsible increased. Even now back home the same thing could have happened. It was one thing to shoot a fellow-man in fair fight, another to strike down the defenceless. There might be some excuse for war; there could be none for murder.

He was correct in supposing the company had broken off the engagement and were occupying the village. They were everywhere, sledges drawn up in the market square and the side streets filled with soldiers, eating their rations. He asked a group of them if they could direct him to Lieutenant Kubik and what had been the outcome of the fight. They said that the lieutenant had been last seen talking with the Herr Hauptmann, who wasn't looking too pleased and they couldn't be far away, that as for the battle it was the same old story of hit-and-run, they'd had a few casualties but the enemy had suffered greater, and more importantly lost several of his precious machine-guns.

Sasha found Lieutenant Kubik with the rest of the company officers as they were breaking up from a conference. People were beginning to come out of their houses again and move about the streets.

Lieutenant Kubik was in the company of Sergeant Karol and a young fair-haired Ukrainian sergeant. It was the latter who saw Sasha first and he attracted the other's attention immediately. All three stopped dead in their tracks and waited for Sasha to come up with them. Kubik made some comment to Sergeant Karol which set him laughing. There was still a smile on the sergeant's lips as Sasha led the horse up to them and halted.

Without a word Kubik stepped to the horse's side and ran his hands first down one leg and then the other.

"He's not hurt, sir," said Sasha.

Kubik made no reply, but looked under the horse, down his withers and flank, and then all over him. Then he said:

"You're lucky to be here."

Sergeant Karol was still smiling and his bright brown eyes looked almost golden. The young Ukrainian sergeant pushed his steel helmet to the back of his head. The snow fell off it and slithered down on to his shoulders.

"That was a fine effort," he said, "When the bastard bolted and you went after him."

Lieutenant Kubik grunted under his breath and said to Sasha:

"Get the horse under cover. It depends upon the storm whether we move off or not. Keep in touch with me."

With no further comment he made off across the marketplace towards the sledges. The Ukrainian touched Sergeant Karol on the shoulder.

"See you later," he said.

"Yes," said Sergeant Karol, his sparkling eyes on Sasha. "See you later."

"There's more shelter round the corner, 'kutscher'," said Sergeant Karol to Sasha.

"Thank you, sir," said Sasha.

"When we get back to headquarters," said Sergeant Karol, the ghost of the smile still on his lips. "If you care to make your application to the Herr Hauptmann in charge of Training I will support it. Maybe we could make a soldier of you, after all. I believe there might be a rifle to spare."

3

Six weeks later Sasha carried a rifle. The battalion marched in infantry formation, along the road to Glybokaie, near the Latvian border; at least that was the direction that little Symon Ravin had overheard Lieutenant Kubik, tell Sergeant Karol as he had ridden past.

Symon had passed the news to Sasha who was now one of the same "gruppe" of No. 1 Platoon of No. 1 Company. Sasha didn't care which way they were going because he was both proud and happy and was content to be marching in any direction as long as it would bring him in contact with the enemy.

The four of them marched in single file on the left hand side of the road. First went Mikita, then Paval Kaluta, followed by Sasha and lastly, little Symon Ravin. At night the four of them shared the same "plandecke." Sergeant Karol, in command, led the platoon and farther ahead, hoping he was looking very important Lieutenant Kubik trotted back and forth alongside the horse-drawn transport. It was April and spring was on the way, though there were still patches of snow here and there and the sledges had given way to carts.

Sergeant Karol had been as good as his word. Sasha was no longer a "kutscher." He was a soldier trusted with a rifle. When they had arrived back in Radzimichy after the sweep around Lake Switaz, Sasha had applied to the Herr Hauptmann in charge of Training and supported by Sergeant Karol's recommendation had been posted to a training company on the outskirts of the town. There he had been issued with a uniform, rifle and equipment which included a "plandecke" —

the triangular waterproof "ground-sheet" with a slit for the head in the centre and which when joined with four other similar triangles formed a tent at night, and in the daytime protected the individual against bad weather.

He had remained with the Commando training company for a month, learning the use of the rifle, elementary tactics in the field, and the meaning of discipline. There had been no time to spare for further training, because the Partisan movement was increasing daily and growing very strong and every man was needed. At this very moment a division of the Field Police was converging on Polotsk in a great encircling round-up. Then, his training completed, he had been granted one day's leave and with mixed feelings of dread and high excitement had gone home.

It had been an unforgettable twelve hours. First of all he had gone to Dubrova, and the first thing he had seen was Valia running through the orchard chasing a mongrel which had sneaked into the kitchen and stolen a lump of fat pork. Darting between the trees with her golden hair streaming out behind her he thought that she looked like a Naiad such as he'd seen in drawings in the art school at Baranovici.

He had called her name and she had stopped in her tracks, whirled round at the sound of his voice and then no longer screaming imprecations against the cur, but with cries of "Sasha! Sasha!" had danced on air, enchantingly, towards him, till their arms were round one another, hugging close in their joy that was between laughter and tears.

When she had recovered and was holding him at arms' length and then in an excess of delight, was hugging him again, she called: "Papa! Papa! See who has come."

Papa was in the harness-room mending the crupper that Sasha had tried to put to rights on that terrible morning following the Partisans' raid when little Sergei Petroff had died. Sasha's fingers had been clumsy with the bad thoughts of that night and the stitching had been indifferent, so that Papa must grumble aloud, and then do the job all over again. Papa hadn't recognized Sasha in his uniform when Valia had led him forward by the hand, and at first he had stared blankly from sister to brother and back again, with a puzzled look on his face. Then quite suddenly Papa had seen who the stranger was and he had given a great shout and flung his arms wide.

Sasha had forgotten that he was supposed to be a soldier and a fighting man and had run forward and laid his head in gratitude and joy that they were all still alive on Papa's breast as if he were a little boy who had been separated from his parents for a very long time.

Papa with his russet-grey hair and stocky figure had stood quite motionless with his son in his arms and his face raised up, while his lips moved and one single tear ran from each eye down his rough jowl and chin which hadn't seen a razor that day. Then after that, when everyone was coherent once more, there were a thousand questions to be answered from both sides.

What was life in the Army like? Oh, it was fine, fine. Was there news of Nicola? — a little hesitant here, since the question in the circumstances was delicate — No! there had been no news of Nicola. He could be anywhere, in the hills, in the forests, or down in the woods by the marshes. But they had heard from Walter and he had had no unwelcome visitors. In fact there had been little seen of the Gestapo for the last month or two. Perhaps the underground movement in Minsk was keeping them too busy. What of Ivan Zavada? Ah, that bad one, no one had seen him for several weeks. Maybe he had obtained what he wanted from another source and had gone to join his friends who also lurked in the dark woods. And the rifle? Yes, Papa had found the rifle with the advent of spring. It was rusty and quite useless and Papa had buried it again, not now under the fickle snow but deep in the trusty earth, where it would never be found.

Then, because he felt he must do so, since nobody however great their immediate joy wanted himself and his people to live in a fool's paradise, Sasha had related how Sergeant Karol had hinted, in so many words as it were, that night in the stable, that Nicola was a Partisan and Sasha was only a "kutscher" because he couldn't as yet be trusted.

Papa said that "as yet" was the operative phrase and that they would all go over to Luba Kumovich's place and see her father Vasil, who in his official position was friendly with one or two German officers' and might have something to say, from his side of the fence. So they had gone over to the Kumovich's house and had found them in.

When they'd asked Vasil if he knew anything about Ivan Zavada, he looked very straight at first and then he blurted out that he knew the devil of a lot. Ivan Zavada had indeed gone to police headquarters, on the day that Sasha had enlisted, so it probably had been Ivan who Sasha had seen on the road to Radzimichy when he had broken his ski. Ivan had laid an information that the Nioman family were pro-Partisan and were concealing arms. No immediate action had been taken because there was insufficient evidence, but the police at Radzimichy had been in touch with the Gestapo headquarters at Minsk and promised to send an interrogating official along. But in the meantime two things had happened.

First of all Ivan Zavada, for reasons best known to himself, had disappeared and so the most important source of information was lacking; and secondly and no less important a

"Kutscher" named Sasha Nioman recently enlisted in the German Field Police, had distinguished himself on the first occasion of coming under fire from the enemy and was deemed by the Herr Hauptmann in charge of Training to be trustworthy, and since he had the makings of a good soldier, worth the trouble and expense of training and equipping.

On both these scores, according to Vasil, the lives and property of Papa and his family would be safe, certainly for the time being, which after all was a very considerable piece of good fortune in times as difficult as these.

All of this then was the reason why Sasha marched gaily, proudly and confidently towards Glybokaie on that early morning of 1944.

The company camped that night just off the road. The men found sticks for their "plandeckes" and crept in beneath them. There was just room to move in Sasha's "plandecke" but that was all to the good for with the four of them huddled close together they managed to keep the cold out. When the summer months came, campaigning such as this would be pleasant. But now at times it could be hard. Before he turned over to sleep, Mikita said:

"Goodnight, everybody. Never say die."

"Never say die," Sasha and Paval repeated. The phrase was becoming a slogan in the platoon. Little Symon said nothing. He was thinking of the endless journeys that lay before them with the terrifying woods on either side. As they passed deeper into the bandit lands the woods would give way to forest. There death could lurk behind every tree. Within his blanket his heart grew cold at the thought.

They left the road and entered the woods at first light of the following day. The rumour had gone round that almost two divisions were operating, so formidable was the Partisan opposition. It was good to see the last of the road with the interminable view of the man in front's back and move forward in line, choosing the path that came easiest through the trees, skirting the undergrowth and attempting to keep in touch with those to right and left.

This, thought Sasha, was the real thing. The feel of the rifle, its weight, its oily odour stimulated within him that feeling of confidence which a firearm always gives. He longed to press the trigger with a bandit in the sights. Behind every truck he fancied he saw a furtive movement, heard a creaking in the branches overhead, caught a fleeting glance of a crouching shadow in a thicket. But no bandit lay in ambush.

By the end of the first day he found the general tension relaxed. Some of the Field Police like Mikita, and particularly Symon, were comparatively old hands, but many more were as inexperienced as himself, and in common with all new troops poured more of themselves into the task than it demanded without preserving the alertness of the old soldier.

On the third night, after he had done duty as sentry the night before, Sasha said before they turned to sleep:

"I call this a farce. I don't believe there's a Communist within a hundred miles."

"If that's so," grumbled Mikita, "we shall still have done a good job and without loss to ourselves in proving that fact. You are too impatient, little rascal. You'll have a bellyful before you're through."

"This kind of fighting," said Paval, who could be sententious, "isn't like any other kind. Most of it is close-range stuff and anything can happen at any moment, particularly when we're in cover like this. I prefer the open where a man can see what he's up to, as the officer said to the lady."

Little Symon, who was the most experienced of all four, contributed nothing to the argument. He came from down south from the Ukraine and longed to be home. He had in fact been homesick for many months now without leave, and with this new job on hand he couldn't see any prospects of a rest. Indeed he had become so accustomed to the tension that he preferred to continue as he was. To return home and relax for a brief, insufficient week would be to unwind the clock so completely that at the climax of its expansion the main spring would over-expand so that it would lose all its resilience and become, to coin a phrase, un-rewindable. Better, he thought, to remain tensed and overwound till the spring snapped.

Either way the result would be identical, the only difference being on the worldly face of it, in one instance the way of cowardice, and in the other of courage. Since he prided himself on being a good soldier the former was unthinkable, so that he accepted the situation as it stood, wondering in a dumb anguished fashion in what manner eventually the end would come and hoping that at least he would put a sufficiently brave face upon it, to conceal his fear. Beneath his blanket he could hear the argument continuing with Sasha saying:

"Well, it's a very good thing if they are a hundred miles away, because I am sure they could have rushed us last night. It was so dark amidst the trees that I couldn't see a thing."

Paval replied: "You can always see in the dark. It's just a matter of getting used to the concentration which is necessary. It's no good just looking into the dark. You've got to concentrate and then you'll see any movement. It gets a bit jumpy sitting out by yourself, doesn't it? But you just get used to it."

"I'm sure you do," said Sasha. "It's good sport really."

"Oh, go to hell, both of you, silly little bastards," said Mikita. "What the hell do you know about sport? I want to go to sleep. Never say 'die'!"

Symon rolled over on his other side. It was perfectly true what Mikita said. What the hell did Sasha or Paval know? It was always the same with these new boys who were given to over confidence. Well, he supposed that was better than boasting. That type was always the first to crack.

But they'd find their own level. Everyone found their level with the Great Leveller. Only the trouble was that its constant proximity drained the strength out of a man just like a woman did, so that it ran out at his finger tips and loins and toes, draining him day and night. Somewhere, very far away, a dog began to howl. Symon looked at his luminous wrist-watch. It was a quarter past midnight. In a couple of hours, he supposed, if he could stop thinking he would be asleep.

Spring seemed to come suddenly. On the fifth day in the forest they woke to find the air was almost balmy. Even when the woods began to thin out giving way to open ground the patches of snow had already melted. The sweep continued and once during the afternoon Sergeant Karol joined Sasha's "gruppe" as they plodded across the plain towards an isolated farm with its low wooden buildings. Some fifteen miles onward the dark line of yet another belt of forest rimmed the horizon.

Sasha grinned up cheerfully as the platoon commander beckoned him to his side, when the line momentarily halted. Far ahead minute forms could be seen moving across their front.

"How is the 'kutscher' progressing?" said Sergeant Karol, but his eyes never left the little dots ahead that were men.

"Now that I am a soldier, sir," said Sasha, "I am happy."

For an instant those brown bright eyes flickered over the younger man.

"You saw your brothers when you went on leave?"

"No, sir. Neither of them."

"Just as well. Keep in good company."

Sergeant Karol took his field-glasses from their case and stared through them. The adjustment must have changed for he lowered them and rotated the eye pieces. Then he put them up to his eyes again. Out on the flank Major Shaeffer and the Herr Hauptmann Weine astride their horses had also drawn up, with glasses levelled. Across the open plain stretched the interminable line of field-grey steel-helmeted figures. Somewhere in the rear, still in the forest, the reserves would be moving slowly forward till the signallers set their field wireless operating and advised them of the check. The little dark specks ahead seemed to have disappeared as if the earth had swallowed them up. A whistle went and the entire line moved on again.

Major Shaeffer and his company commander rode along the line until they came opposite Sergeant Karol, and the two officers turned their horses to keep pace with him.

"What did you make of it, sergeant?" said Major Shaeffer.

"It could have been, Herr Major," said Sergeant Karol.

Sasha, trudging along just behind his platoon commander took stock of the Herr Major, half-turned in the saddle in order to continue his conversation. He was tall and lean and fair, with a straight back that kept him bolt upright in a firm seat, and a long leg that swung easily to the stirrup from the clamped knee. There was a hint of grey in his clipped moustache and in the cropped hair at the side of his head. His eye was blue and keen, his manner graceful, his charm complete.

"If we don't contact and engage by the next forest belt," he said to the Herr Hauptmann, "We shall take to the roads and jump the next ten miles by lorry. There's said to be a concentration beyond Polotsk and on this side of the Dvina."

"Very good, Herr Major."

They rode off in their separate directions and Sergeant Karol moved along the last "gruppe" of his platoon. Dusk began to fall as the long line of men straggling across the plain approached the dark outline of the woods which had persisted in their eye-line since the mid-morning. The battalion halted by companies and with their half-company pickets posted began to dig in and bivouac for the night a mile from the forest. With his stomach full of a hot swill which went by the name of stew Sasha lay in his "plandecke" with his blanket. The stars glittered overhead and it was growing cold.

"If we don't catch the bandits during the next forty-eight hours," said Sasha, "We shall move on to Polotsk by lorry."

"Where did you get that from?" said Paval.

"Sergeant Karol and Major Shaeffer," said Sasha.

"At a conference, I suppose," said Mikita. "A conference specially held for that little rascal Sasha Nioman, so they could all ask his advice from Herr Himmler downwards."

"It's the truth anyway. I overheard it."

"The only way that the common soldier gets to know anything about the battle he's taking part in," said Paval, "Is by eavesdropping or being on an orderly room staff half a million miles behind the line. Well, tomorrow we shall see if you are right. Maybe, we shall catch up with your Partisans before then."

"Or maybe not," said Mikita yawning. "Who the hell cares as long as somebody ends this bloody silly war."

"Which we shall win," said Sasha. "And then we shall get our country back. Oh, yes we shall. We shall be a free nation again."

"Go to Hell," said Mikita. "Who cares about any bloody nation as long as there's plenty of vodka and the women are keen. Goodnight. Never say 'die'."

An hour after first light the whole line moved forward towards the forest. The air was electric with rumour as so often persists with troops under strain. The distant unidentified specks of men which had prompted a halt during the previous afternoon had been seen no more. Had they been friend or foe, or merely labourers from a collective farm, bound on their lawful occasions? One rumour had it that they were the last of a screen of a rear-guard action that was imminent since the encirclement was completed and that as soon as the battalion entered the dense woods they would be met with ferocious delaying tactics. Again it was common talk that far from being concerned with a retreat, those distant figures had been indicative of an enemy about to launch an attack and that as soon as the German line advanced a murderous and terrific counter-blow would be struck.

The very appearance of the forest inspired suspicion. Sasha trudged his way across the rising ground immediately ahead with Paval on one side of him and Symon the other. About the centre of the platoon Mikita lumbered cheerfully along in the rear of Sergeant Karol.

The ground after a thousand yards rose still more sharply to where a promontory of the forest squatted like a giant toad on the crest of the slope. It appeared singularly sinister at this distance. A ground mist hung like a halo round the hill so that the boles of the trees were obscured and the heavy intertangled canopy of branches and twigs seemed poised without support in mid-air.

Sasha, struggling up the incline, was not surprised to see Symon some paces behind panting with the effort and his face shining with perspiration. Even so he carried his weapon unslung and at the ready and every now and again the corner of his mouth would drag itself down in an involuntary twitch.

"Keep going," said Sasha. "We'll soon be there."

It struck him at the time as a particularly fatuous remark because he of all people hadn't the vaguest idea whither they might be bound, but the moment seemed to call for some word of encouragement because in the grey light of that early hour Symon looked ill and drawn. Moreover, the wan and sickly smile with its hint of ingratiation which Sasha received in return was, he found, a little disquieting. Nor did he like the way in which Symon constantly licked his lips. Then, almost shoulder to shoulder, with the long line of their comrades wading shoulder high through the mist, they were inside the forest.

Immediately they seemed to be in another world. As they passed, as it were, the threshold, the trees themselves seemed to lock arms in a cordon behind them and shut them off with a barrier of solid wood from all sentient life. The ground was heavy beneath their feet with sodden moss which squelched as they trod upon it. At the foot of the trees giant toadstools grew and a spotted fleshy lichen, leprous and repulsive, clung to the bark. Here it seemed the seasons would have no part; and here for ever, from time immemorial to the unborn ages to come, the primordial forest would remain withdrawn within itself in its eternal gloom.

They could see one another but dimly as they moved forward, as each one picked his own path. Now and again someone would stare into the skyless, arborean canopy above and a safety catch would click; sometimes a subdued chattering would break out to be abruptly silenced by an order, but for the most part the battalion advanced in a sort of awed silence, as if all things about them were poised, hesitant, tense for the inevitable something which must surely happen at any moment.

As the morning progressed, Sasha felt himself becoming dispirited. Already they must have done endless miles through the close-set trees; at times he wondered how much longer it would be before they would see the sun again. Once or twice a ray of light would filter fitfully through from above, then it would become absorbed into the all-pervading shadows.

By noon the day, with its complete lack of incident, its dispiriting silence, its increasing strain at every step forward which must bring them closer to their waiting, watching, enemy, had become almost intolerable. Every man was feeling the effects of prolonged nervous exhaustion. Even Mikita had ceased to make jokes at his neighbours. Now he plodded on with a sort of sullen determination.

As the hours passed the suspense increased. Even the old hands became restless, and once a man grown careless through overstrained nerves, stumbled so that his tommy-gun suddenly began to chatter as it slipped from his hand and struck the ground.

The sound billowing through the forest, seemingly picking up its own echo and repeating it, sent every man darting behind cover and the line of its own accord brought itself to a halt. When it moved on again it received no orders to do so, but lunged forward drunkenly, sagging in the centre. Veterans, accustomed to this kind of warfare, grinned derision in self-defence, at the newcomers but were themselves far from immune from the pervading sense of impending disaster that seemed to hang over everyone.

Symon caught Sasha's eye and winked ostentatiously and quite unconvincingly. Sasha, more honestly, said:

"Why doesn't someone start screaming and clear the air?"

Sergeant Karol moved down the line of his platoon and a few paces ahead of them, from time to time mingling with the men or calling to an Oberfeldwebel to spread his "gruppe" out more or to close it in. He was perfectly well aware of the futility of such an instruction which owing to the increasing density of the undergrowth could not always be implemented; but he was too experienced an N.C.O. not to know the value to the men of a sight of their commander and the sound of his voice. After all good soldiers were primarily hounds who needed a huntsman and his horn to control and guide them.

Dusk began to fall, but still the sweep continued. The silence became over-bearing with the deepening of the shadows. Sasha wondered, when night came, what form of bivouacs would be ordered. It would be wet beneath the trees even under a "plandecke" because the ground was saturated with its own sweating. It began to rain as the thought passed through his mind.

The drops fell heavily, threshing through the branches till the sound was like that of surf on a foreshore. Sasha took the "plandecke" from his shoulder, unrolled it and put his head through the hole. He kept his rifle underneath the waterproof drill because the weapon was his most prized possession, his very pride and joy. He could scarcely bear to see a speck of mud nor a finger stain anywhere upon it.

The sudden blinding flash and the roar of the first explosion set him staggering. His steel-helmet fell across his forehead. He pushed it back with his free hand while he clutched his rifle with the other. The second explosion knocked him off his feet. He picked himself up but remained on all-fours, panting and gasping. For six interminable seconds there was silence in the forest as though the entire battalion had been stunned. He looked across his shoulder in Symon's direction. He was standing with his back to a tree, his hands on either side of him pressed against the trunk. It was as if he were holding on for support and his eyes were glazed as in a trance. Then on the instant a man nearby began to scream in agony.

Instantly a clamour of orders broke out. Everyone was to hold their ground and take cover. It was precisely what everyone was doing and the order seemed to Sasha ridiculous. The wounded man continued to scream, a hideous and bloodcurdling sound. It went on and on and someone shouted:

"For Christ's sake, stop that bloody noise."

It was Sergeant Karol's voice. Sasha could see him. He was crawling forward towards a writhing figure on the ground and he carried his entrenching tool in his hand. The screaming had struck a higher pitch. Sasha thought if the sound didn't stop soon it would drive him off his head, but Sergeant Karol had reached the wounded man. He raised his right hand twice, and twice it fell. Thereafter there was no more screaming. Somebody said:

"Serve the bastard right."

Minutes later an extraordinary, small but persistent sound attracted Sasha's attention. It came from where Symon still stood petrified. It was like the subdued rattling of castanets. Symon's teeth were chattering and he could no more stop the sound than stop the war. Sasha thought it was rather contemptible and the sound embarrassed him in the same way as Symon's self-effacing smile.

Someone in the immediate rear — it sounded like Lieutenant Kubik's voice — seemed to be trying to organize something. He was calling out names but it was difficult to see who responded because of the trees and the failing light. The rain, after its first fierce onset, had changed to a steady drizzle.

Sasha sank to the soft ground and settled down to wait. The men to right and left started their speculative grumbling and now and again a bolt clicked or a magazine rattled. Beyond the first two explosions there had been no sign of the enemy. The forest seemed deathly quiet and waiting. When another quarter of an hour had passed Symon joined him and laid down beside him. They could hear Mikita talking to Paval:

"What the hell's all this about? Where's that little rascal, Sasha Nioman? I bet he's at the back of this, some of his mischief. Where are you Sasha Nioman., you little devil?"

Sasha was about to reply when Sergeant Karol called:

"Cut that cackle. Every man remain where he is." Then, adding as makeweight: "You're a bloody nuisance, Mikita Tomko."

"What's happening?" whispered Sasha to Symon. "What's it all about?"

"I'm not certain," said Symon. He had regained control of himself but he was occasionally shaken by a sudden fit of shuddering.

Sasha wondered if signs like these were the beginnings of shell-shock; he'd heard something to that effect before, so he said to Symon, not unkindly:

"Do you think you've been shell-shocked?"

"No," said Symon, adding surprisingly, "I wish I had."

"Wish you had?" said Sasha "Wish you had! What a thing to say! Why do you say that Symon Ravin? I don't understand —"

There was another sudden rumbling roar down where the fourth company must be. Then another, followed by five more in rapid succession. Then came a medley of subdued shouting and the sound of whistles. The sounds died away almost at once.

"Are they attacking?" said Sasha.

"No," said Symon. "We should have heard their fire by now."

"Then what was all that?" said Sasha.

"Mines," said Symon.

The battalion slept that night where it had halted, all, that is, except the half company on the right flank who had stumbled on the evacuated Partisan camp. Twice during the night there were further explosions when some more daring than the others and wearied of the penetrating rain ventured into the deserted, heavily mined camp; but there was no indication whatsoever of the former occupants. Once again the birds had flown. When morning came, after a quiet night with no other alarm, the battalion moved on.

At eleven o'clock the sun came out and the forest ended with the same abrupt line of demarcation as it had begun. Ahead the ground fell steeply away in a fine and sweeping incline and the cloud shadows chased each other up the opposite slope. In the elbow of the valley a long road twined its way towards the north-east. Sasha stood at the fringe of the forest, drawing in great draughts of the sweet and wine-like air. It had been an unpleasant night but now it was morning and magnificent. What more could a man of sixteen years and nearly nine months desire than to stand on the brink of such a hill as this with a dark, dread forest behind him, and before him hope and the April sun? What more indeed when he could add to that the knowledge that he was a proud member of the greatest fighting machine that man had ever made? Then he saw at the foot of the valley, just where the road came into sight, the first of the lorries taking the corner. Two hours later the battalion were all aboard and the long motorized column was moving steadily in the direction of Polotsk.

Mikita Tomko, squatting with his back against the side of a lorry, nursing his tommy-gun on his knee, took a worn post-card size photo out of his uniform pocket. He regarded it lovingly. The amiable Fraulein beamed back at him. Then he caught Sasha's eyes upon him. He reversed the photograph so that Sasha could see it.

"Next leave we marry," he said. Then he winked hugely. "My Davina," he said. "I could eat her."

4

They were ten miles south of Polotsk by mid-afternoon of the same day. The convoy drew up where the road ran straight along a hill-crest with the fields falling away to the familiar shallow valley on either side. The battalion tumbled out of the trucks and took to the fields once more forming the line of their sweep.

Everyone knew the situation now. They were moving up in support of the Rumanian Legionnaires on the left flank, in order to strengthen the line. There were further reserves in their own rear and the pressure was being increased because the Partisans appeared to be trapped with their backs to the Dvina. Very soon now the jaws of the vice would close.

By evening No. 1 Company with No. 2 and No. 3 on its right had moved two miles forward and were digging in for the night. A further mile ahead another chain of small woods, linked with stretches of scrub, ran across the German front. There was no sign of the enemy as each company posted its pickets and detailed the watches. The light went out in the sky gradually, and the air was warm. Spring was on the move.

Under the "plandecke", wrapped in his blanket warm and tired, Sasha turned to sleep with the murmur of the others' voices in his ears. He told himself that altogether it had been quite a good day after a night of strain. They were hard on the tracks of the enemy and a decision would soon be forced. But the memory of Sergeant Karol beating at a writhing figure with the handle of his entrenching tool persisted. He found Sergeant Karol an enigma and wondered if he had noticed little

Symon Ravin's nervous tic. He wouldn't mind betting that Sergeant Karol would soon deal with that.

Then he fell to wondering what Symon had really meant by that odd answer to his question of shell-shock. "I wish I had," Symon had said. He supposed that Symon had had enough of it and was getting a bit beyond it all, like old Kubik. Well, as for the Lieutenant, he would have him know he wasn't a "kutscher" any more. He was a soldier now and that was no mean achievement. Like Mikita he'd prove himself a good soldier. Anyway he knew whom he hated now and that made things easier. If a man had to fight he needs must hate. He dismissed a momentary vision of the grave in the garden and a white blotched face like a clown's from his mind and instantly fell asleep.

He woke with all the sudden clamour of battle in his ears. One moment it was dead silence, the next the fury was in full blast. He rolled out of his blanket, grabbed his rifle, and crawled to the edge of the "fox-hole".

The air was full of red tracer. The burning bullets curved through the night in long swooping flights like a rain of golden fire. He knew that between every drop of that gleaming rain, ten other invisible bullets filled the gap. They could cut a man's trunk in half like the rasping, ragged cut of a gigantic circular saw.

In the rear the battalion's half battery of four 105 millimetre field guns sounded like a giant hammering a tin tray. When last Sasha had heard them he had taken no part in the fight, being sheltered in a farmyard with old Kubik's horse, and the guns had had a sort of barking, hiccoughing sound. Now close to, they had a more distinct twang and a clang of their own. On either flank the machine-guns were thudding and clattering and the rifle fire crackled.

He knew what to do and began to open fire on the prearranged fixed line to cover the front with cross-fire. As he emptied his magazine into the darkness a strange exaltation possessed him. At every kick of the rifle butt into his shoulder he gritted his teeth and said: "Take that, you bastards." He was quite well aware that he would be lucky if one of his bullets found a mark, but every time he pulled the trigger he felt the joy rush into his throat.

It was not too dark to see something of the struggle that was taking place. The enemy fire was pouring from the woods in front in rapid and concentrated bursts. Every now and again in reply a salvo from the field guns would burst amongst the trees and light them with a momentary lurid glare. There was heavy machine-gunning on the right of No. 3 Company and between No. 2 Company's left flank, and it seemed from the crash of grenades and the shouting that hand-to-hand fighting was in progress. Above all the tumult of battle, time after time the Partisan war-cry "For Stalin and Russia" was ringing out.

Symon, lying beside Sasha, was firing methodically, calmly reloading and firing again. He seemed in action to be a different man from the nervous wreck of the forest. Mikita lay on the other side grunting each time he pressed the trigger and farther along Paval crouched at the low parapet directing bursts of his tommy-gun into the darkness.

Sasha shouted in Mikita's ear:

"Do you know what's happening?"

"Of course I don't," yelled Mikita. "Except that it's just an excuse for wasting ammunition — look out!"

A flare had gone up, leaving its trail of golden sparks behind it. Now it had burst into the fierce incandescence of burning calcium. Immediately all that lay below was etched into shapes of inky black or blinding white. The four men in their shallow pit pressed close to the earth, but they could see across the storm of bullets, the staggering, advancing line of the Partisan's tremendous assault. Regardless of the ferocity of the German cross-fire, the bursting shrapnel, and the massed rifle fire, the terrible and desperate advance surged nearer and nearer. Another flare went up and another sector of the battlefield was illuminated. As far as the eye could see a dark, struggling, cursing mass of men was plunging forwards. Locked in their death-grip they fell in heaps but those behind leapt across their comrades' bodies and the irresistible tidal wave rolled on.

It plunged like a solid breaker between No. 1 and No. 2 Companies. There was no longer any reason to rely upon the fixed lines and hope for the best. Now it was just a matter of emptying a magazine almost at point-blank range into the exposed flank of the enemy.

They went down in scores with their battle cry in their throats. They swept headlong through the gap which they had driven, by sheer strength of arms and determination, between the two companies. They spilled into the open country behind the broken line, fanned out and pressed on. But still the main forces of the Communist guerrillas stood with their backs to the Dvina.

Sergeant Karol came leaping from trench to shallow trench, twisting and dodging as he ran. He reached Sasha's fox-hole and flung himself down.

"Have they broken through?" he shouted.

Another flare went up. There seemed to be some sort of movement far to the right but there was none at all to their immediate front. Except for the stream of machine-gun fire whipping over the ground and the occasional crash of shrapnel from high above and the resultant smack of its bullets on the ground, there might never have been an assault.

"Are they through?" repeated Sergeant Karol.

"Some of them," said Sasha.

Sergeant Karol fumbled at his belt. He drew out a Verey pistol.

"I'll give No. 2 a 'white'," he said. "Then if we get a 'green' answer back, the four of you get on out to the right and make contact with the others. We've got to close the gap."

The fire from the woods had become desultory, with an occasional vicious burst. Machine-guns, under the light of another flare seemed to have found a target. Sergeant Karol laid down the pistol and flung up his night-glasses.

"They've broken through the line," he said.

He replaced his glasses and raised the pistol. He pressed the trigger and the rocket soared aloft to break into a ball of white.

"Wait for it," said Sergeant Karol. "Do you know how many got through?"

"I couldn't see all that," said Sasha. "It was a fearful muddle."

An answering green light broke in the sky a quarter of a mile away to the right.

"There you are," said Sergeant Karol. "That's No. 2 answering. Don't trouble about those bastards who got through. They won't interfere with you. They've got their own troubles to attend to, but we'll have most of them 'mopped up' by the morning or my name isn't Karol. Now get going and keep your eyes open.

The desperate night assault of the Partisans to break the German line before the Dvina had begun at midnight. It was five o'clock in the evening when Sasha stumbled upon the Oberfeldwebel with the ten soldiers of No. 2 Company and formed the link that closed the gap.

By nine o'clock of the following morning, with the main body of the enemy retiring towards the distant river, the entire German line prepared to advance. The trap was closing.

5

Half an hour before zero hour arrived, the first of the enemy who had been some of the first to break through during the night to make contact with the Germans were five Byelorussians from the neighbourhood of Radzimichy. They were lost and had come in to give themselves up. The second party numbered a hundred including three women. They had been "mopped up" and brought in by a detachment of the reserves, who handed their prisoners over and immediately departed. The prisoners squatted on their haunches not a dozen yards from Sasha's fox-hole while the Herr Hauptmann, in command of the sector, called a hurried conference. Ten minutes later, Sergeant Karol, beckoned Sasha up to him.

"You can attend to that one," he said.

He pointed to a fair-haired Byelorussian who had been among the first five to surrender. He was a round-faced, snub-nosed youngster.

"Sir?" said Sasha enquiringly, being slightly puzzled.

"Take him away and shoot him," said Sergeant Karol, referring to his field note-book. There was much to occupy his mind.

"Shoot who?" said Sasha.

"That bastard there," said Karol impatiently. "We're taking no prisoners. It's an order."

Sasha's heart gave a great thump and he felt his mouth go dry.

"I am a member of your platoon, sir," he heard himself saying. "And not of a Gestapo execution squad."

Sergeant Karol, who had turned aside to more important affairs, spun round as if he'd received a blow in the back.

"*What?*" he said incredulously.

"I'm not going to kill a man in cold blood," said Sasha.

"You're going to obey an order, or —" said Sergeant Karol and he slipped a hand to the pistol butt in his holster.

Sasha felt himself beginning to tremble all over, but it was with indignation as much as fear. For the moment words failed him, so he shook his head vehemently.

Sergeant Karol stared at Sasha as if he were some rare and curious creature he had seen for the first time. The sergeant's golden brown eyes glittered and his hand closed over the butt of the weapon which he had now drawn.

"You refuse to obey my command?"

"Yes, if you must put it like that," said Sasha and his voice was hardly above a whisper.

"Do you realize what it means? I'm entitled to deal with you in the same way as I've told you to deal with the prisoner."

"It's still my answer, sir," said Sasha.

They faced one another for fully five seconds. The rain was beginning again and a spot fell on Sasha's cheek. He wondered if it was the last time he would feel rain on his face. Sergeant Karol's regard never faltered though his eyebrow was cocked in a quizzical way. Then with an exclamation of exasperation he thrust his pistol back in its holster and looked around him to where his men stood waiting in groups for the order to continue the general advance.

"Here you," he said, and he pointed to an anti-Communist by the name of Stiapan Arkasni, who was slightly known to Sasha.

Stiapan ran swiftly to his commander.

"You call me, Sergeant?"

"Take that man away and shoot him."

"Ja whol, at once," said Stiapari.

He clicked the heels of his jack-boots as Sergeant Karol turned away and strode over to one of his corporals. Then he winked at Sasha and grinned broadly. He patted the automatic rifle over his shoulder, then he unslung it.

"What kind of a man are you," said Sasha with quivering lips, "to shoot defenceless men?"

"Now listen, little man, don't talk crap. You're new to this business and another Communist out of the way, the happier I am." And with that he sauntered over to where the prisoner sat with his legs drawn up under him. He prodded him with his foot.

"Get up," he said. "You and I have an appointment together."

A look of bewilderment, and then dawning realization and ultimate terror overspread the other's features. His big mouth opened in a slobber and two tears of panic rolled down his cheeks.

"Get up," said Stiapan. "Our appointment is private," and he jerked his head towards a nearby thicket.

The prisoner fell forward on his face and he caught at Stiapan's feet in supplication, but Stiapan kicked his fingers off his boots so that he began to yelp with the pain and several people looked round.

"Get up," said Stiapan again, "Unless you want it here in the back."

He put his hand in the other's leather belt and lugged him to his feet. Then at the point of the rifle, one before the other, they set off towards the little wood. Once the prisoner turned with his hands clasped before him, as if he would drop upon his knees, but Stiapan caught him by the throat and swung him

141

round. Almost immediately after Sasha heard the sound of a single shot.

The second party of some hundred prisoners required more detailed organization. The remaining four Byelorussians were ordered to join the others and the whole party was then marched under escort to the empty stables of a nearby farm. The homestead itself had been partially destroyed in the battle of the previous night, and the farmer and his family had long since fled. The escort was provided by No. 2 Company but additional assistance was provided by No. 1 Company in order to dissipate the factual details should there be at any time in the future a leakage of information, throughout a countryside which it was necessary to a certain degree, to placate. Sasha was detailed for the additional escort on the instructions of Sergeant Karol. He overheard the order being given and fell in with the No. 2 Company guards as the prisoners in ragged column of route were marched past. They numbered just over one hundred men, with a few women among them.

They were indeed a scare-crow mob, with every conceivable kind of garment from tattered lambskin caps to outworn sheepskin jerkins, from patched leather breeches to German infantry issue trousers, purloined in some former raid. A few were truculent, but the majority appeared resigned to their fate. The barbed wire of the concentration camp and slow starvation was the best they could expect.

Sasha was glad, to be detailed for this duty for it gave him the chance to scan the faces as they passed, expecting as always to see Nicola's among them. But there was none resembling the beloved elder brother and it was with relief that he hastened to obey the Oberfeldwebel's order to proceed to the farm buildings and report what straw was available.

There was straw in plenty. A stack had remained intact and untouched by the shell-fire that had shattered the farmhouse and several of the outbuildings. He ran back to the slowly advancing, column of bedraggled prisoners and reported his find to the corporal.

"Good. We are putting this carrion in the stables. See if you can find a pitch-fork or two in one of the buildings and set to work yourself and get as much straw across to the stables as you can." The corporal grinned; "We want to see them nicely bedded down."

By the time the column arrived, dragging their weary muddied feet through the gateway of the farmyard, Sasha had managed to find three pitch-forks and had himself carried from the stack to the stable door the equivalent of a couple of trusses.

The escort halted the prisoners before the stable door which was thrown open. One of the women started to wail in a high pitched keening voice that sent the chill running down Sasha's spine. He paused and watched, leaning on his pitch fork, his rifle slung across his back as the guards began to force their captives into the narrow stalls. At the best eighty men would have found considerable difficulty in finding room, now just over one hundred were packed in. When any fell they were rifle-butted to their feet or clubbed to insensibility against the cobbles of the yard, and then dragged in to join their fellows.

Meanwhile two of the guards had helped themselves to the other two pitch-forks and the rest of the escort were gathered round the stack, clawing out handfuls of straw and carrying them across to the walls of the stable. Very soon all that remained of the stack was a litter in the yard where it had stood. The bolts had been shot across the stable door and the straw stood over two feet high round the exterior walls.

A sense of dread and impending horror filled Sasha. Although Sergeant Karol was nowhere near, was indeed a hundred yards away moving amongst the men giving and passing on orders — it seemed to Sasha that he was once again looking directly into the sergeant's mocking eyes. And now the escort was bringing up four heavy calibre machine guns of the water-cooled type and were mounting them forty yards from each corner of the building and directed towards it.

The Oberfeldwebel was issuing curt instructions and two men were running up and down the length of the stable walls spilling the contents of two buckets in cupfuls on to the piled straw. From where he stood Sasha could smell the unmistakable odour of petrol. From the interior of the stable came a muffled but steady murmur of raucous voices and a sound like a subdued trampling of feet. A woman began to shout.

As the two men darting back emptied the buckets tilting the last of their contents into the already saturated straw, the corporal flung a lit fuse.

There was one tremendous, stunning roar of ignition. The blast of sudden heat scorched Sasha's face as he reeled back. Then the flames were soaring twice the height of the wooden building and one appalling eldritch screech of agony arose from within. The sound rose higher and higher above the clamour of the flames and the crackling timbers, so that Sasha plugged both his ears with his thumbs, but he could not fail to see what was happening.

The building was already a furnace. In its white hot core flame-enveloped forms could be seen momentarily staggering then dropping and disappearing. At the extremities of the blazing inferno where it burnt flickering yellow and scarlet, other darker forms with their clothing alight staggered out of the funeral pyre, spinning like Catherine wheels, or toppling to the cobbled yard spouting fire.

Then, to make certain because this was an order, the machine-guns spoke and poured burst after burst into the seething mass. Very soon all that remained was a great heap of red-hot embers in whose heart an indistinguishable mass hissed and sizzled like roasting pork.

A whistle was sounding by the line of fox-holes and orders were being shouted. Sasha dropped the pitch-fork and unslung his rifle. He carried it at the trail as he dashed up to rejoin his platoon. He came into the line as the order for the advance was signalled. Sergeant Karol waved his men on. Over his shoulder he appeared to notice Sasha because he glanced back again. His dark handsome face and flashing eyes still had that quizzical look in them.

"Come along there," he cried. "Keep up abreast. All together and keep going."

Mikita ranged up alongside Sasha.

"Noisy bastard," said Mikita cheerfully, "But he's a good soldier. What do you say, Sasha Nioman, you little rascal? What do you say?"

Sasha gritted his teeth.

"Oh! never say die," he said.

The slow advance continued.

6

The rain continued with scarcely an interval for three and a half days. At night the men scraped their holes in the ground and took what shelter they could under their "plandecke's," but the shallow trenches soon became water-logged and scarcely habitable. Sasha longed for the summer to come when it would be pleasant to shelter from the sun in the shade of a great tree and not as now crouch beneath it with the rain-drops dripping down his neck.

For three days the battalion drove forward through a forest so dense that even in daylight the companies lost touch with each other from time to time and must make their whereabouts known with a signal rocket. At night the coloured identification Verey lights lit the sky and tinted the tree tops so that sentries perched far off, high on precarious boughs could distinguish the position of the various units. But it was not until the morning of the fourth day that contact was re-established with the retreating enemy. Then as the leading company emerged from the forest they were met with a withering fire from across the Dvina.

Whatever arguments might have been produced in the past that the enemy was trapped must now be dispelled. He was across the river in force, and strongly entrenched. How he had contrived a crossing at this point in the strong current and in so desolate a district with no bridge for many miles, was beyond conjecture. It was only reasonable to presume he had swum over and carried his equipment with him — in itself a heroic feat.

But he had brought his machine-guns and automatic weapons across and now judging by the account he was giving of himself, he was none the worse for the immersion. No. 1 Company, taken by surprise as they left the wood, immediately suffered heavy casualties. There had been no signs of the Partisans nor their emplacements from this side of the Dvina and the scout-screen had been deceived by the innocent appearance of the south bank. Nor had they suspected the presence of the enemy until they themselves had reached the reeds that fringed the brink of the swirling dangerous waters, and received a sudden fierce burst of fire that scattered them.

That night dug-in as well as might be under constant observation of the enemy and his almost continual machine-gunning, Sasha took his watch as sentry as the rain suddenly ceased and a watery moon came out from a bank of low and rapidly disintegrating cloud.

He lay in a forward observation pit with his beloved rifle lying at hand and propped across the low parapet. He could see just behind the crest of a high bank the gleam and glitter of the Dvina as she flowed past. Not far off in the next and double observation pit Paval Kaluta talked in low undertones with little Symon Ravin, who also stood their watch. The former was extolling the virtues of Mikita Tomko who, two hundred yards in the rear, was rolled in his blanket and snoring with the gusto of a war-horse.

"He has no sense of fear," said Paval. "He is a splendid man."

"Perhaps he has no imagination," said Symon.

"Do you think," said Paval, "that some men are born cowards and others heroes?"

"I think," said Symon, "That all men are born equal and that it is circumstances which shape them."

"That is ridiculous," said Paval. "I think man makes the circumstances. It is always the first step that counts. If one should do a brave thing and win a good medal, then that is encouragement to do the same again."

"I don't think it always works out that way. Quiet, listen. Is that something by the river?"

For several seconds they listened intently. There was no sound but the rustle of the eddies along the high bank.

"I hear nothing. There is something the matter with your nerves, Symon Ravin."

"My nerves are all right," said Symon testily. "But I could have sworn I heard something."

"What could you possibly hear? Everybody knows they cannot have any boats to cross and make a surprise attack. You will be seeing your own ghost yet."

"Perhaps I shall," said Symon.

Four hours before dawn with the express purpose of forcing the passage of the Dvina, three infantry companies together with an engineer field company, arrived as reinforcements.

At first all went well. The entrenched enemy unaware of any additional threat made no attempt to molest the engineers who made good progress with their wooden bridge till it had reached well past mid-stream. Then as dawn came, suddenly realizing what was taking place, the Partisans poured a murderous fire into the forward party working on the raft nearest their own shore. Five men — technicians who could ill be spared — fell at once, and another was swept away into the vicious current.

Immediately replacements were called for to man the devastated raft. Sasha withdrawing from his post as the light crept into the sky could observe with his companions the entire proceedings.

He saw with justifiable pride — since he too now was part of the Wehrmacht — how the engineer company pressed forward in the face of severe opposition with great courage and determination. Despite all the efforts of the enemy, who at one time even ventured across the open ground on their side of the river and attempted to establish sites for his heavy machine-guns, the Storm Troopers on the heels of their engineers swarmed over the fragile bridge as soon as the last section was made fast. Then fanning out on the far bank they gave supporting fire as platoon by platoon and company by company the Field Police Battalion scampered across.

Not since his first brief baptism of fire as a "kutscher" had Sasha felt so scared. Despite its hideous aftermath he had exulted in the night-fight of the Partisan break-through. There had been a feeling of grim satisfaction in giving back as good as had been received; now as he made his dash across the bridge with half a dozen others before him and a score more waiting for their turn, he felt as once before that inexplicable sensation of utter nakedness.

The enemy machine-gun bullets were skimming the water in a wicked cross-fire. They thudded into the timbers of the rafts and set the splinters flying. Now and again a better judged burst would sweep knee-high across the lashings so that men mown down as with a gigantic scythe were swept from feet and legs that were part of them no longer. They toppled into the swirling river whose blood-stained waters threatened to burst the crazy bridge apart.

Sasha reached the other side bent double and expecting every second to be his last. Behind him he could hear the bark of 105 millimetre guns and the whine and whistle of their shells as they passed over his head.

But the barrage was taking effect. The advanced enemy machine gun posts were being driven back as Sasha leapt ashore. Then he was dashing helter-skelter for a rise in the ground where he could see Symon Ravin with several others of the platoon firing steadily to his front.

Sasha dropped down beside Symon, who cast one hurried glance at him and without making any further sign of recognition returned to his task. Two hundred yards ahead a wood began to disintegrate as the "105s" concentrated their fire on it.

Whole trees seemed to split down the length of their trunks, spring suddenly into the air, crumple and collapse. At the same time the order was given for the general advance and the German line went forward.

It went forward by sections at times controlled, at times haphazard. Machine-gun fire blazed from the wood and men stumbled and fell and rose again only to fall once more. The wood ahead crackled and splintered with the steel tempest let loose upon it, and at its fringe the line surged and swayed, and finally each man and each sector struggling on its own account, gained its shelter as the barrage lifted and crept forward, lifted and fell again.

There was no opposition from within the wood now. The battalion, momentarily exhausted, awaited the inevitable counter-attack; with the remnants of the badly mauled Storm Troops, they clung on to the hardly won position.

The attack never came. Reserves still swarming across the Dvina were by now moving up in scores in support of the dauntless battalion and the open ground between the river and the wood was dotted with converging groups of men. As they reached the forward line on the fringe of the wood, the barrage lifted and at the same time the order came to advance once more.

They opened in half-companies into the well-known skirmishing order, passing amidst trees shattered with gun-fire and strewn with corpses at their feet, but now like another never-to-be-forgotten forest, strangely silent.

The sudden lull in the battle gave Sasha the opportunity to take stock of the situation. As far as he could apprehend he was amongst No. 2 Company, because he could see Lieutenant Kubik between the trees, but beyond Symon and Paval who were on either side of him, there was no sign of any other members of his own platoon. In the crossing of the river everyone seemed to have become inextricably mixed. However, he supposed, that was a minor issue since they could all sort themselves out at the end of the action, provided of course, there were sufficient of them left to sort out, because casualties had been heavy on both sides and the wood was carpeted with dead and wounded.

But one thing was certain. If the storm had for the moment lost something of its fury, on their emergence at the far side of the wood it could break out again into a veritable tempest. The enemy was on the run but he was by no means destroyed.

This time they came out from the shelter of the shattered trees with extreme caution, the scouts creeping and crawling cautiously forward. The Herr Hauptmann Weine with the company headquarters staff on the edge of the wood was one of the first to receive information. He scanned the open ground before him through his field-glasses and what he beheld brought a low, tuneless whistling to his lips which was his way when he was satisfied that what he saw was what he had been confident he would see. It was a habit which he frequently employed when in the company of senior officers who had doubted his word, and had the effect of driving them to impotent fury, though no one had ever dared to prefer a charge of dumb insolence against him. For the rest he was strikingly handsome with a long, aquiline nose and cruel thin lips with a pencil-line moustache. There was now a trickle of blood down his cheek where a bullet had grazed him, but the blood had dried. He had purposely not wiped it away when wet.

What he saw now were four enemy "pill-boxes" ranged before yet another wood, nearly a hundred and fifty paces apart and positioned in a rough echelon to render the supporting enfilade fire of each the more effective. They had been improvised from wooden legs, neatly dove-tailed like a log cabin, and on top earth and twigs packed tightly together reinforced the roof.

The Herr Hauptmann, an experienced campaigner and as ruthless as he was debonair, thought that the Partisans for all their lack of field training had made a very good job of the series of strong-posts and that anyone tackling them would have to have more than his wits about him. Therefore he scribbled a message on a sheet from his field note-book, because the signallers with their wireless still lagged behind, and gave it to a runner telling him to find the anti-tank section and to make it as quick as hell. Then he took to studying the pill-boxes again and when he lowered his glasses he was whistling more tunelessly than ever. Nevertheless he felt he had to prove that he was right so he gave an order. It was the sort of order of which Lieutenant Kubik in his turn often doubted the wisdom.

The Herr Hauptmann snapped to the Zug-Wachtmeister at his side:

"Pass the word along for the company to attack the strong-post on the extreme right, in individual rushes."

The sergeant stared for a moment as if he'd not heard aright since he considered that the order bordered on madness. It was not the responsibility of a company commander to issue instructions for an attack when his battalion commander was nearby, moreover the field artillery had not as yet come up.

Nevertheless stranger things had happened before when the Herr Hauptmann had been proved right, and after all these Field Police, for all their soldierly ways were really only legionnaires, and a few more off the ration strength wouldn't be noticed. It was not as if they were the Wehrmacht proper. Moreover, it was not for a sergeant to question the command of a captain.

The order reached Lieutenant Kubik's platoon before Sergeant Karol's. As was right and proper the Lieutenant set the example and after passing the order on, was the first to dash forward with some half dozen of his men. This was clearly the conduct of a good officer; it was also the decision of a crafty soldier who knew that the first to start an action before the enemy could properly align his sights would be more certain of survival than those who followed when he was alerted. Such points as these were, in Lieutenant Kubik's opinion, the finer nuances in the ineffable act of tragi-comedy called war.

No shots at all greeted the Lieutenant's magnificent display of initiative. It was only when the last "gruppe" of his platoon began to move that the enemy appeared to become interested. Then the instant the section moved a devastating burst of fire swept four men gathered together in a bunch out of existence.

Sergeant Karol cursing his company commander under his breath for the rash damn fool he was, rapped out the order to advance by individual rushes. Five men including Paval Kaluta stumbled to their feet as the whole company opened with covering fire. Almost at once Paval fell.

The opposition from the strong posts was formidable. The machine-gunners seemed to have some agreed code. Their overlapping was so neatly timed that on a gun jamming or the re-loading of a belt, there appeared to be no apparent interruption of their fire. The bark of the trees before which the battalion lay was stripped by their traversing fire as if a giant rasp had been drawn along the long line of trunks. Somewhere in the depths of the same wood a "Zug-Wachtmeister" was decoding a message asking for the support of the anti-tank guns. The crews with their long-nosed weapons set off at a run between the trees. They seemed to know who had sent for them.

Paval Kaluta was kicking his heels in the air, not fifty paces from Sasha. Great clods of earth whirled over the latter's head as he lay prone, his head tucked into his shoulders. A stray bullet passed close to him, struck the extreme edge of the back rim of his steel helmet which jerked it back and downwards on to the nape of his neck. He thought for the moment he had been scalped and his neck broken. When he dared to raise his head he could see no sign of Paval's legs.

At his side Symon was shouting:

"We've got to get him in!"

His face was grimed with mud and there were livid rivulets where the sweat had poured down his cheeks. He looked for all the world like some wild warrior in all his full war-paint. At another time Sasha would have burst out laughing.

"Get who in?" he yelled.

"Paval's lying out there. We've got to get him in."

"Hell to that!" said Sasha.

"You've got to help me," said Symon. "We can't leave him out there."

"Leave him and we'll pick him up when we go forward," said Sasha.

"We shan't go forward. They'll drive us back. You know what they'll do to Paval if they get him. We've got to get him in."

Somewhere on the edge of the wood the anti-tank gunners were creeping into position. A mortar battery to their right flank opened fire. The first salvo fell short landing twenty yards in front of the second pill-box. The solid ground spouted sods and chunks of earth. The second salvo landed plumb on the reinforced roof. There was a burst of cheering along the line, but there seemed no visible effect on the pillbox. Then the anti-tank guns opened up. Their armour-piercing shells began to penetrate the wooden logs of the strong posts. There seemed something might be said for Hauptmann Weine's decision after all.

"Come on," screamed Symon.

It seemed to Sasha that the other was demented, but he followed him. Symon was wriggling his way forward foot by foot, belly to earth and digging the toes of his boots in. His rifle was slung across his back and he was pushing his rolled "plandecke" before him, seemingly as some sort of cover.

Sasha rose as far as his hands and knees. The second pill-box was on fire and he caught a glimpse of figures breaking out with their arms and hands locked before their faces and staggering through the flames. The machine-gunning from the other three strong posts poured in a deadly fire on the prostrate battalion. Sasha felt a sudden pain on the cheek of his right buttock as if a red-hot rod had momentarily been pressed against it. He dropped flat. When he dared to move his hand it met the bare flesh. As he took his fingers away he found them covered with blood. He felt very little pain and began to laugh in a high, hysterical fashion because this was the funniest thing that had ever happened to anybody. If he survived this action he would be able to tell all the world that he'd attempted to rescue Paval like a hero and got shot in the bottom for his trouble.

Nevertheless he crawled on after Symon. Someone was yelling from the rear to come back for the love of God and it sounded like Sergeant Karol's voice, but Sasha couldn't be sure. The clamour of the battle rose to a crescendo as the anti-tank guns continued to attack.

Sasha and Symon reached Paval at the same moment. He lay flat on his back with his mouth gaping, but his eyes were open. As Symon touched his hand he turned his head and a look of recognition came into his face.

Symon propped him up by the shoulders while Sasha attempted to work the outspread "plandecke" underneath him. Between them they managed to slide Paval on to the waterproof sheet. Sasha was still giggling helplessly at the thought of his flesh-wound. Symon swore at him and the battle surged about them. But they dragged Paval on the "plandecke" yard by painful yard and sometimes he helped with his hands like a swimmer on his back. His legs seemed useless though he appeared to be in no pain. Within a quarter of an hour they had progressed twenty-five yards back towards their own line. It was necessary from time to time to flatten out when the ground began to shake and the bullets drummed too closely overhead. Ten minutes later they were still five yards from the first recumbent figure. Three of the enemy pill-boxes were now ablaze with their resistance suddenly and astonishingly reduced to a desultory half-hearted spluttering. Sasha and

Symon rose to their feet as the entire line sprang forward, surging past them. The roar of the battle had dropped to an undertone.

"There," said Symon to Paval, where he lay. "You're safe."

He was trembling and white-faced. Sasha was furtively feeling at his own backside.

"Leave him for the stretcher-bearers."

This time Sasha was sure that it was Sergeant Karol's voice, but though he looked all around and through the press of men, in the general confusion forward, he could catch no sight of the sergeant.

"Get on with it," said Sasha to Symon. "He'll be all right now, won't you, Paval? Buck up, Paval, never say die."

Then he dropped on his knee because Paval's mouth was sagging more widely open than ever and his head had rolled to one side and he lay very still.

"They've killed him!" said Sasha incredulously as if such an event was a rarity. Then he joined Symon who was already walking away to regain the others as they advanced upon the now silent and smoking pill-boxes.

That night the battalion dug in. The Partisans, as observed by aerial reconnaissance, were in full flight, and all other reports confirmed that they had lost almost two-thirds of their strength, and had split up into small groups. The operation had proved successful. There was no need to venture farther, but should the enemy rally and reform, merely wait for any subsequent attack that might come. He neither regrouped nor attacked. He had had enough.

In the last week of April all four companies were taken by lorry to Lapy where they entrained for Maladechna in West Byelorussia. From there they detrained and marched to Krasna, a hundred miles west of Minsk.

At Krasna, Symon Ravin of the 34th Battalion Field Police received the decoration of the Guerrilla Warfare Medal in bronze, with its skull and cross-bones and four writhing snakes and the swastika, the whole enclosed in an oval floral wreath. The award was made for gallantry in the field when he had gone to the rescue of a wounded comrade since deceased. Everybody, with one exception, was delighted that little Symon's courage should have received due recognition.

The exception was Symon Ravin himself. He had desired no decoration which needs must be lived up to, but rather a wound which would have put him out of the war or, since the long anguish was rapidly approaching the uttermost limit, quick death itself.

Sasha received promotion. He was relieved of his rifle, and was given as a special mark, of honour and trust a Smeisser. He spent many hours with his new toy, taking it to pieces and oiling it and then putting it together again. His wound — it was little more than a graze — healed rapidly. As Mikita said, both Sasha and Symon now bore the marks of battle, one of which was a medal which should be worn on the chest. The joke, such as it was, went the rounds of the battalion.

7

On 3 May, 1944, the battalion left Krasna for a six weeks' operation against Partisans supported by Russian paratroopers who had been dropped behind the front line.

There had been several replacements and newcomers to the company and to No. 1 Platoon, which Sergeant Karol, whose approaching promotion to commissioned rank was rumoured, still commanded. Hauptmann Weine commanded the company and Lieutenant Kubik still survived. Major Shaeffer was in charge of the battalion though it was on the cards that he might go up to Oberst after the former successful sweep. Nevertheless, there were newcomers of which three in particular were posted to No. 1 Platoon.

There was, first of all, Kurt Hermann. He was twenty-two years of age and had served some desperate weeks, so he said, in the front line with the Wehrmacht before Stalingrad. It soon became apparent that he took umbrage at a posting to a unit which he considered beneath his dignity and military record. He implied, moreover, that he was a member of the Wehrmacht and averse to serving alongside legionnaires. Symon loathed him as an upstart and a braggart. Mikita voiced his opinion openly that he was a bar and wanted to know why, if what he implied was true, he should have been posted to the Field Police unless he had proved unsatisfactory with the regulars. He was moreover one of the kind which are legion, who know the answer to everything, but he was of Polish origin and that seemed to cover many of his sins.

Secondly, Michas Shamso arrived to replace a casualty whose wound had gone septic and had led to an amputation above the knee. Sasha thought of Michas as someone not far removed from a saint. He was a Ukrainian and the same age as Kurt, but whereas the latter was loud-mouthed and emphatic, Michas was mild and gentle, and with features of such rare spiritual beauty that the first time Sasha saw him he remembered a description which Nicola had once read to him, of St. Paul: "When he smiled his face was like that of an angel."

Kurt took an obscene delight in bragging of his less reputable occasions with women in Michas' company and Mikita sexually wholesome as he was, confided to Sasha that he thought Michas a bit of a prig. Sasha, confronted with the conclusions of so matured a mind of twenty-two, could only mumble an inadequate word or two which satisfied Mikita. Nevertheless, as the days passed he was to observe how the tone of any conversation, however ill-informed, illiterate or mildly disgusting, always tended to change to a higher level in the presence of Michas, who would never express one word of disapproval or raise a critical eye. It was indeed as if his presence, without any conscious effort on his part, was enough to dissipate all evil things. In time Mikita fell under the spell as well as Sasha, though little Symon Ravin, in his deep torment, loved Michas from the very start. But Kurt stuck out his chin, and stretched his neck, and swaggered and strutted unnecessarily when Michas was in the vicinity, and though everyone knew that deep within himself Michas was laughing at Kurt for the fool he was making of himself, not the tremor of a smile nor the twinkle of an eye revealed those thoughts.

The third newcomer was called Josip Polyn who was a Byelorussian and had served his time as an artist in the Art School of Baranovici. To some extent he kept himself remote from the others, only putting forth an opinion when some outrageous comment flung at random across the barrack-room exasperated him to such an extent he could contain himself no longer. He would then embark upon an exposition that was above everyone's head, except perhaps Michas's, and then retreat into a silence from which no one could arouse him. Much of his time in off-duty hours he spent with his charcoal and chalks, and water-colour box. He was tall and lean with legs like a spider whereas Kurt, who despised him, was bull-necked, close-cropped and bow-legged. Sasha thought that, for a mixed bag, they were excellent company on the whole.

Over these three newcomers, the three older hands, and the rest of his command, Sergeant Karol the inscrutable, watched with his shining eyes, appraising them as fellow-men and soldiers, but always as soldiers first.

It was raining when the battalion moved from Krasna to join the division near Minsk and it continued through the first fortnight of the hard fighting north of Borysov where joined by yet another division they successfully encircled the better part of some ten thousand guerrillas of which six thousand were destroyed though the remainder managed to escape capture and death.

Thereafter for the next three weeks, with the Partisans on the run and retreating steadily to the east, the division split up into regiments and at times so many were the pockets of resistance springing up on every side, into even smaller units, that frequently the 34th Battalion Field Police found itself working on its own, an unsupported unit responsible for the elimination of all those "bandits" within its allotted area.

Therefore the sentiments of Paval, whose grave was marked by yet another of the inevitable, impersonal wooden crosses of heroes departed, could be all the more easily recognized as bearing the stamp of truth, in that all that a private soldier ever knew of any battle was only what was taking place on his own immediate sector, and what they conceived to be correct could be in fact, the very opposite of what was happening when viewed in the overall picture presented to headquarters. The division, regiment, battalion and even company could as independent units in the cruel guerrilla warfare win or lose a local battle while a score of miles off, the very reverse had occurred. The occupied lands, seething like a cauldron, could seemingly appear to be mastered, but away to the east the front line, like a steel wire strung to breaking tension, could suddenly snap.

But all the way to Borisov and fifteen miles to the north-west of the town the little red devils of victory pranced and chirruped on Sasha's shoulders. Despite the support of Russian paratroops which had now become a commonplace in the enemy plan, the "bandits" appeared to be on the run.

And the rain stopped and the sun came out. No longer did the trees of the forest drip moistly and miserably, and no longer did the sodden moss give way without warning in a morass. The sun shone through the branches and the thick leaves. On a warm June night, it was pleasant to sleep beneath a star-spangled sky.

It was good, Sasha felt, to have such stout comrades-in-arms as those beside him, and good to be one of such a tried and trusted company. Because, he told himself, that was what they were, what he himself now was; one of a band trusted and true, and proved in battle.

The early summer of 1944, as far as Sasha was concerned, was turning out surprisingly to be a period of considerable satisfaction and contentment. Only at times memory of Nicola would return and then sometimes on watch in the small hours of the morning or curled in his blanket at night, the strong, proven man that was Sasha Nioman, would unaccountedly become a small and lonely boy again, and the horn-pipe song of the little red devils would change to the ghost-like whine of a small, lost soul winging its aimless way through the limbo of the damned.

By the end of June the battalion found itself sweeping up the slopes of the high ground that lay fifteen miles north-west of Borisov. There had been an exchange of volleys in the valley and the Partisans had been seen scattering up the opposite slope and then out of range taking to the woods that crowned the summits.

A consultation with his maps told Major Shaeffer and his company commanders that this was no forest that confronted them but sparse woodland giving way to open country beyond. Two companies, one of infantry and one of horse, were detailed to make a detour under cover of the high ground to the enemy rear while a frontal attack would hold the enemy with two half-companies on either flank developing the enfilade.

Distances were confirmed and the estimated time of attack decided upon and all watches checked. Major Shaeffer dismissed his commanders and their subordinates, and with twenty minutes in hand in which the platoon officers could outline the scheme to their N.C.O.s, took his field-glasses and examined the enemy position.

It was now mid-morning of a fine, cloudless day with the promise of genuine heat by noon. There was movement near the woods ahead where the Partisans awaited the next development. The Major found the spectacle of the distant trees in their new green, and the peaceful downland that led up to the first of their ranks, very pleasing to the eye. High above him a lark was shrilling in the sky. There was some modicum of contentment in him, despite the fact that the Germans by now had evacuated practically all of Russia with the exception of a wide arc around Minsk. Within the hour the enemy — and he hoped there would be some genuine Russian regulars amongst them! — would be receiving yet another trouncing.

At the appointed hour the operation commenced. Sasha and the five friends of his "gruppe" went forward immediately behind Sergeant Karol, while the remainder of No. 2 Company who formed the spear-head of the frontal attack were extended in skirmishing order. Ahead of them lay the distant wood, but each man knew he was a sitting target for an enemy who would hold fire till the last moment; moreover, everyone realized that not only was it part of their commander's plan they should draw the enemy fire so that he should disclose his position with certainty, but that Major Shaeffer would without a shadow of doubt have, as usual, something up his sleeve. Even so, Sasha found it more than a little nerve-racking plodding on under a cloudless sky and a bright morning sun expecting every second that the shimmering wood on the horizon would erupt with rifle fire. Nevertheless, he told himself, the thin line of scouts would take the sting out of the first blow, and if what he surmised were correct, by the time that happened the enfilading companies would be in position on the flanks and the Partisans would find they were in a trap. Therefore he trudged on, confident like the others that Major Shaeffer knew precisely what he was doing and any lives that might be forfeit through his scheme, were a justifiable risk.

No movement, no sound, came from the wood, which drowsed on under the mounting sun, and as he progressed Sasha's boots became yellow with dust. He looked to right and left and saw the bronzed faces of his comrades and his eyes fell on Mikita swinging along with his head thrown back and his splendid sinewed neck bare; on little Symon trotting to keep up and pulling off the feathered ends of the tall grass as he passed; on Kurt with his square jaw set, and Michas with the sweet, rare smile on his lips. He caught Josip's eye and the latter wrinkled his nose, and put his tongue out at him.

And Sasha burst out laughing, for this was a deathly game of cat-and-mouse and hide-and-seek with no quarter asked or given on either side, nevertheless it was the finest sport of all. Beasts hunted other beasts because that was their necessity, and man hunted the beasts in turn, sometimes because of his need and sometimes for the fun of it. But when in deadly earnest, man hunted man, then that was the greatest hunt of all.

The sound of the aeroplane which had been a half-recognized murmur in his inner ear became suddenly a noisy reality. He looked up, shielding his eyes against the sun. As the machine began to circle the long line of the advance, he saw that it was an old out-dated biplane with an open cock-pit for a pilot and observer. He couldn't name it, because aircraft-identification wasn't one of his strong points, but he wondered idly why it should trouble to make circuits above the 34th Battalion who were engaged in nothing at all out of the ordinary and very seldom asked or received air support. Then as he watched as it came round again he saw the observer in his rear seat lean out and the next moment some small object was turning over and over in the air as it made its way to the ground.

The moment it struck a volume of thick yellow smoke began to rise. There was no explosion and no sign of fire. Sasha, who was nearest to this strange missile, cupped his mouth to call out to Sergeant Karol when Kurt began to run towards him gesticulating and shouting:

"Pick it up, Sasha Nioman. It is a signal."

But now Sergeant Karol's attention had been attracted, and he too was moving rapidly to where the smoke was pouring up from the ground like a miniature volcano.

Sasha was the first to reach the spot. He saw that the yellow fumes were issuing from one end of a container, the other end of which was fastened with a screw-top. Kurt who was up to him by now picked up the container, undid the screw-top, and drew out a paper. It was a Service form with a message scrawled in German. Sasha looked up inquiringly at Kurt as the latter perused it, turned it over, studied it again.

"What is it?" said Sasha. Even then the advent of this spectacular object which he had never seen before seemed portentous.

"I don't know," said Kurt. "It's addressed to All Officers Commanding Forces in the Field."

The aeroplane was now a little black speck dwindling in the sky, and the sound of its propeller was scarcely audible.

"Give it to me," said Sergeant Karol, who had drawn level. On either side the skirmishers moved steadily forward. Mikita and Symon were several yards ahead by now, but Lieutenant Kubik was running back and Josip was halted and staring in their direction. Sergeant Karol was frowning as he read the message and his lower lip was pushed out in a pugnacious sort of way. Then his eyes lifted from the paper and met Sasha's.

There was a curious look on his face and quite unfathomable. It was as if he were taking Sasha into his confidence and he gave an odd little contemptuous nod of the head and the merest shrug of the shoulders as if to imply; "I told you so." Encouraged, Sasha asked:

"What is it, Sergeant Karol?"

The look passed from Sergeant Karol's face almost as soon as it came, his sparkling eyes went cold and unfriendly.

"An Order," said Sergeant Karol. He handed the form over to Lieutenant Kubik who had reached his side. The Lieutenant read it.

"Well," he said, "That can only mean one thing."

"Maybe," said Sergeant Karol. "But how are we to know?"

A shot rang out from the wood, then another. The scouts and skirmishers went flat on their faces and a machine-gun began to talk.

"Here you," said Lieutenant Kubik to Sasha. "Find Major Shaeffer and take this to him and do it quickly."

The engagement ahead of the little group was becoming general. Far out on the right flank the heads of the enfilading company were beginning to appear over a ridge. Very soon the same thing would be happening on the opposite side and in the rear the cavalry were awaiting the signal to slam fast the back door. The battalion commander's tactics were succeeding.

Sasha found Major Shaeffer with Hauptmann Henkel, his second-in-command, a sergeant and two runners. They were seated behind an isolated thicket with their field-glasses levelled on the wood. Behind the thicket their "kutscher" waited with their horses. There was a slackening of the enemy fire and both enfilading companies were beginning to advance in short rushes. It would not be long now before another area was declared "clear."

The sergeant took the message from Sasha and tapped the Herr Hauptmann on the shoulder.

"What is it?" said Hauptmann Henkel, lowering his glasses, then seeing the message, snatched it and read it. He was a heavily built man of forty-eight, with a double chin and a little pouting mouth like a carp. He seemed to be short-sighted because he held the paper not four inches from his nose. There was a purplish bloom like that of a plum over his big flabby cheeks, and when he was perturbed a crimson flush stained his forehead. At all times the whites of his eyes were a bilious yellow.

"What the hell do they think they are doing?" he exploded.

Major Shaeffer turned his face from his glasses and held out his hand for the message. He read it through once then turned to study the enemy position again, then he opened his hand where the paper lay crumpled and once more read it. There was the sound of shouting from the wood and a momentary flashing amidst the trees.

"What do you make of it?" said Hauptmann Henkel.

"I'll give it another hour," said the Major. "Take no prisoners."

"I'm talking about the signal," said the Hauptmann.

"Oh, that," said Shaeffer. He slipped the folded message into his breast pocket. "I've no doubt High Command know their business."

"If I thought —" and the Hauptmann lowered his voice. "If I thought there was any truth in what I am thinking … in what you and I... both of us are thinking … in view of everything and what kind of retaliation we could expect... No prisoners did you say?"

"No prisoners," said Major Shaeffer.

The brief action ended just after five o'clock of the afternoon. Two hundred and fifty Partisans altogether were killed. There were no survivors. Half an hour later the battalion was assembled in dispersal formation along a secondary road running east and west. Inattentive to the command to march and accustomed to the one direction only, Sasha turned to his right instead of his left and colliding, stumbled face to face into the man next to him.

"Keep your ears open, you little rascal," growled Mikita.

Sasha recovered himself and turned about. He blinked his eye because the sun was beginning to complete its arc towards eventide. To his surprise, he found that he had only at that moment realized that the battalion had begun its "about turn" retreat towards the west.

8

They fell back on Minsk. It was two days' march and the horse waggons carried the rations and ammunition. Every now and again transport and men would be forced close to the road-side to let the mechanized columns pass through. The lorries were full of men of the Wehrmacht infantry regiments. There were occasions, moreover, when the panzers took up all the road, clattering past. The soldiers in the lorries and the tank crews all looked cheerful and in good health. The movement towards the west — it had not yet been recognized among the lower ranks as a retreat — was orderly and disciplined. There was no loss of morale.

It was night when the battalion reached Minsk. All day long the Wehrmacht columns had passed to the west in seemingly endless streams.

The Germans as the Russians steadily advanced were making very certain that their picked troops should escape. They went by lorry. It was only the likes of the legionnaires that could be left to their fate. Many of them had long since learned to read between the lines.

When the battalion reached Minsk the Russian bombs were falling.

The roar and rumble of the falling bombs was an answer to the situation, in itself. The Cossacks might still be many miles distant, but the enemy air force could reach out and find their target. The battalion ration and ammunition waggons by-passed the city by a secondary eastern route while the faster moving convoys of the Wehrmacht swung off to the west. When the battalion transport once again struck the main road beyond the outskirts of Minsk the regular troops were still farther ahead. Meanwhile the battalion itself had marched through the town and unwarned, had been caught in the bombardment. There had been several casualties, but the march continued through the night till they reached a village some twenty miles beyond the city where they bivouacked. Sasha noticed that only two "gruppes" in contrast to the customary two companies, were detailed and posted as pickets. Nevertheless he was confident that Major Shaeffer as a commander fully understood his job and he supposed that three factors prompted a decision which in other circumstances he would have put down to an unforgivable negligence.

The three factors which reassured him were: first the great distance between themselves and the front-line despite whatever might have taken place there; secondly the Partisans in all the area over which the battalion had been operating had been either destroyed or forced to disperse into such small groups that no one party of its own accord could present any danger; and thirdly that even if any of the scattered bands were preparing to reform, the battalion by reason of the speed of its march to the west was out of reach. Nevertheless, the unanswered questions that kept re-occurring, the mystery and ill-informed rumours that surrounded their present movements, and the lack of information, together with the day-long, night-long traffic pressing on to the west, convoy on convoy, created an uneasy feeling that all was not well. It had been so easy, on the crest of personal successes, to call "Never say die," even to a dying man. Now, whatever excuses might be made there was a feeling that somebody had left a door open in the back of the house and the draught was blowing through and was distinctly chilly.

They set out for Stolpcy the following morning, having paraded an hour late since it had been past midnight when they had bedded down the night before. If there had been any apparent uneasiness, the fresh bright morning seemed to have dissipated it. Everyone was in good spirits and the talk among themselves was when the Wehrmacht would halt and make a stand, and what part they themselves would play. Then suddenly at half past one in the afternoon three Yak-1 Fighters in line-ahead, came roaring down the Stolpcy road. So little had been seen of Russian fighters at any time that aircraft identification had played a very secondary part in the battalion's training, and now the first warning they had of an attack was the sudden thudding vibration of the air, the roar of engines, and a hail of bullets that mowed down a dozen men at the first burst.

The Yaks swooped down the length of the column leaving a trail of dead and dying in their wake. There was no retaliation from the battalion taken by surprise and the three aircraft soared away into the blue converging as they reformed till a man's hand could have covered their span of sky.

Sasha's "Gruppe" had been untouched though the blast of the machine-guns had for the moment deafened them. He crawled out from the ditch where he had flung himself and fell into place again as they resumed their march, wondering all the time when the next attack might develop, because this was something new and very alarming.

It was, he told himself, not so much the speed and destruction nor the element of surprise and the consequent torment of suspense, that gave the presence of enemy fighters such significance, but the fact that considering their limited range they were clearly within striking distance of the retreating

German forces, and therefore the enemy's advance was meeting with less resistance than might have been expected.

Retreating forces? He caught himself up at the phrase. Ever since the signal-flare on the last round-up they had been marching swiftly to the west. It was now four days and three nights of it. All the time, except through the passage through the capital, the Wehrmacht convoys had borne steadily on, a never-ending, nose-to-tail procession. And this was the road which within only another twenty miles or so could lead, if a well-known by-road were taken, to his own home and to Haradischa itself.

He could hear once more, far ahead as the afternoon lengthened and he grew hot beneath the July sun, the rattle of machine-gunning and the rapid-fire reply of "flak" and knew that somewhere farther on where a dusty road passed over a shoulder of the ground, another Russian sortie was finding its target. That was why, he felt sure, that the battalion was not taking the brunt of any attack, since the Wehrmacht were far bigger game, but nevertheless the constant strain and suspense were very tiring.

For the first time since he had joined the platoon he felt dispirited. The perspiration kept gathering at the nape of his neck and trickling down his spine and his chest was running with sweat. His mouth was dry with the summer dust and his eyes felt hot and heavy. Wherever they might bivouac for the night he would be glad to reach the end of this day's journey. Maybe tomorrow would see a turn in their fortunes, and perhaps after all, the ebb tide was not so strong as it appeared to be. In fact, nobody else to all appearances seemed unduly disheartened, so no doubt this sense of depression was peculiar to himself. But this was one of the times he needed Nicola.

His spirits flagged at the thought of his loss. If Nicola was here he would say the right word, the brave and cheerful word, that would make all the difference. But Nicola wasn't here and for all he knew he could be lying crumpled and dead or burnt to ashes. Even one of his own wild bullets could have found their way into Nicola's vitals that night the Partisans had made their break-through when the Communist forces had stood with their backs to the Dvina. He tramped on, feeling that his feet would very soon burst their boots.

They camped that night in a wood six miles from Stolpcy and a day's march from Radzimichy. The wood was sweet-smelling and cool and a little stream trickled through it. After the heat of the day it was splendid to rinse and bathe and he lay half-stripped on an outspread "plandecke," with companions on either side. The road to Stolpcy ran through the wood, cutting it in two. Two companies occupied the right of the road and the other two were on the left with the field battery and the horses. None of the guns were positioned and nobody had been detailed for picket-duty. When the evening rations had been eaten the time came for smoking, before the officer of the day, whoever it might be, made his rounds.

Sasha lay outstretched on his back and let the light breeze play over his flesh. It was a delicious feeling, and after a meal the mood of depression began to disappear. The six of them of Sasha's "gruppe" sprawled alongside him, and the cool evening painted the bright green trees gold and amber to anyone lying at ease and staring upwards through that emerald lattice to the sky.

"The Major!" said Mikita, "has gone to Radzimichy, and taken Sergeant Karol with him. Don't ask me how I know because I saw him go, so that old fool Hauptmann Henkel is in command. And don't ask me why the Major has gone to

Radzimichy because I don't know, but my guess is that he has gone to our headquarters for instructions, now that we have got ourselves into this bloody mess."

"Who says it's a bloody mess?" demanded Kurt. He lay on his face naked, his chin on his forearm. "The Generals know what they are doing."

"Let's forget this damn war," said Josip Polyn. "Just for five minutes."

"How can anyone forget it," said Kurt in his surly way. "Why should we want to? Isn't it what we're here for?"

"You may be," said Josip. "So you can speak for yourself, but at this very moment I should prefer to be in my Tania's room in the art school at Baranovici —"

"And who was Tania?" said Mikita, rolling over on his side.

"My model," said Josip, for once growing expansive. "Such legs —"

"Better than yours," said Kurt. "Who's detailed for picket?"

No one replied. Kurt sat up and circled his knees with his bare, brown arms. For all his dour ill-looks and close-cropped Nazi head, his body was magnificent with the muscles rippling under the satin skin. Now with the late sunlight glancing through the trees, and gilding him from shoulder to ankle, he looked like a faun come up from the crystal stream where he had bathed. Sasha clad in shirt and trousers but with his sore feet still bare, marvelled at the beauty of the half-stripped figures around him and he knew that once again a picture was before him which would never fade.

"Who's detailed for picket?" Kurt repeated. He picked up his shirt and began to pull it over his head.

"Nobody's been detailed," said Michas. "Sergeant Karol left before he made his rounds."

"We'll share out the watches, turn and turn about," said Kurt. "The same as we did before Stalingrad where we were left on our own. We've got to do our picket. Even if everyone else has forgotten how to look after themselves."

"I'm the senior," said Mikita. "I'll choose the last watch."

"So will I," said Sasha. "I'll share it with you."

By ten o'clock the greater part of all four companies were asleep.

9

Sunday, 2 July, dawned bright and clear, with scarcely a cloud in the sky. Such was the feeling of security that only one "gruppe" of No. 1 Platoon of No. 1 Company had troubled to keep any kind of watch. At Divisional Headquarters at Radzimichy Major Shaeffer and Sergeant Karol slept in beds for the first time for many weeks, while under an improvised shelter of ground-sheets and branches Hauptmann Henkel lay on his back with his mouth open, and snoring so loudly that Hauptmann Weine was forced to move away in disgust to another part of the wood.

Sasha was on guard with Mikita Tomko as the light came into the sky. They lay side by side in the long grass of a meadow on the north side of the wood. There was a narrow belt of ground-mist half-way across the field but with the first rays of the sun it quickly dispersed. A quarter of an hour after first light, when their watch ended both Sasha and Mikita heard the sound of artillery fire from the direction of Stolpcy.

An artillery duel as distinct from aerial bombardment was in progress. The sound after the first few rounds became a regular drum-fire. In a very short time it was possible on occasions to distinguish the calibre of a salvo and then the drum-fire would re-commence.

"That is artillery," said Mikita.

"That's what I was thinking," said Sasha.

With a shifting of the wind the sound of the cannonade became more distinct.

"That is heavy artillery firing," said Mikita. "I don't think it can be more than ten miles away."

"It seems to be drawing closer," said Sasha.

From the corner of his eye he could see Lieutenant Kubik and two other Wehrmacht officers emerging from the edge of the wood. They stood together talking quietly amongst themselves. Kubik held up his hand for silence as the rumble of the distant guns momentarily increased.

"Drawing closer?" said Mikita. "No, just a change of wind. I wonder whose guns are those, little rascal?"

He nodded grimly to himself, then he looked Sasha steadily in the eye.

"Those won't be Partisan guns," he said slowly. "Because the bandits *don't possess any artillery*!"

He rose to his feet.

"Let us go and see what the Herr Lieutenant, the poor half-wit, has to tell us," he said. "Do you feel that it might be on the cards, little rascal, that quite a big surprise might be in store for us? Come, let's go and see what the clever ones have to say."

The two of them made their way through the long dewy grass towards the group of officers. The sun was beginning to touch the tops of the trees. Mikita saluted so punctiliously that in the circumstances the gesture seemed almost exaggerated, and a flicker of annoyance passed across Lieutenant Kubik's face as he returned the compliment.

"Well," he said abruptly. "What can I do for you? I've seen you before, haven't I? Ah, yes, I remember. Subversive and insolent." His eye fell on Sasha. "Ah, the 'kutscher'," he said.

His regard returned in Mikita's direction.

"Well," he said. "What is it? What do you want?"

"I was wondering if you had heard the guns, sir," said Mikita.

"Of course I heard the guns," said Lieutenant Kubik irritably. "They're loud enough, aren't they?"

"Indeed they are," said Mikita. "But I was wondering."

"Every time you start wondering," said the Lieutenant, "do you have to inflict your thoughts upon an officer without as much as by-your-leave?"

"Not if I knew whose guns they were," said Mikita significantly.

The three officers exchanged glances. Then one of them nodded and drew out a pocket-book. He laboriously pencilled a message in block capitals, tore out the page and folded it in two.

"Take this to Hauptmann Henkel. You'll find him in his hide-out," he said as Hauptmann Weine strolled out of the wood. The Hauptmann was smoking a cigarette whose ash he tapped off with a forefinger.

"Ah, Kubik!" he said. "You are about early."

"The guns disturbed me," said Lieutenant Kubik.

"Indeed," said Weine. "The guns — ah, of course the guns. Whose do you think they might be? Interesting and curious. Nobody seems to have put out any pickets last night. I think we're getting very slack. Perhaps we shall get a rude awakening one day." He gave a grin, entirely without any semblance of mirth.

The rumble of the distant cannonade rose and fell. Deep in the wood Sasha and Mikita searched for their commander. They found him fast asleep and still snoring. Mikita woke him with a steady shaking of the shoulder, so that he sat up swearing, and rubbing the sleep from his eyes.

"Who the hell are you?" he said. "What do you want?"

Mikita handed him the scrap of paper and he snatched it from him and began to read.

"Unidentified gunfire —" he said. "Oh! the devil take it. This would happen when Shaeffer isn't here." And then to Sasha and his companion, "What the hell are you staring at? Get to the devil out of here. No! get my servant," He began to shout.

"Andrei! Andrei! Where the hell is the fellow?"

A voice from a nearby thicket called:

"Coming sir... coming ..."

"Take a message," said Hauptmann Henkel to Sasha. "Take this down and don't stand there gaping like a congenital idiot. God knows what things are coming to. Now get this down and get across the road to the cavalry lines and give this message to Lieutenant Schneider."

Sasha fumbled for a pencil, found a stub of one, while Mikita produced an envelope. It appeared that there were no message-blocks at battalion headquarters.

"Get this down," said Hauptman Henkel, struggling with his knee-boots. "To Lieutenant Schneider, from Officer Commanding No. 34 Battalion. Immediate. Dispatch cavalry reconnaissance to investigate unidentified gun fire. Report on return. Message over. Now get out of my sight."

It was approaching five o'clock when Sasha found Lieutenant Schneider near the horse-lines. The lieutenant was still in his pyjamas which he invariably carried with him. The contents of the message appeared to infuriate him.

"I haven't heard any gun-fire," No doubt his sleep had been deep. "And what if I had? How like Henkel to throw a fit because someone's having a bit of a battle. What if they are? The bandits can't be in force after the hiding we've given them —"

"I don't think the Partisans are engaged, sir," said Mikita.

"You don't think the — What do you mean?"

"The Partisans haven't any heavy guns, sir."

"The Partisans haven't any — What the hell are you talking about?"

180

"It could be the Russians, sir," said Mikita.

"It could be the — Oh! Glory to God, whatever next! Impossible! Do you know how far behind the lines we are? How fast they'd have to travel to reach us?" He glared at Sasha. "I don't know where they find them," he commented. He began to draw on his breeches.

Twenty minutes later, Sasha and Mikita watched the two troops of mounted infantry form up in the wood, then wheel right and set off at a brisk pace along the road to Stolpcy. There were a hundred mounted men in all, and the sound of their horses hooves made a merry clatter together with their jingling bits. Sasha thought they made a pretty picture, and wondered what they would find and have to report when they returned.

"I think, said Mikita, "That we will go back to where we were." "Our watch is over —" began Sasha.

"So I understand, little rascal," said Mikita. "Nevertheless, I think we will be wise to return and still continue our watch. I do not think that Lieutenant Schneider has any sense, nor for that matter have any of the others except perhaps Hauptmann Weine."

He held up his hand as he stopped to listen.

"It is growing quieter," he said at last.

"Maybe the battle's over," said Sasha "And we are alarming ourselves unnecessarily. When the cavalry report back —"

"If they do," said Mikita. "Come, let us take up our old positions."

The battalion on all. sides was stirring as they passed through the wood. It was breakfast time and a fine morning after a good night's sleep. Within the centre of the encampment spirits were high. It was only on the northern fringe of the wood where No. 1 Company had spent the night and had alone posted their pickets, that men's voices were being raised in what might have been taken for anger.

Sasha could hear the comments as they passed by. "Talk sense, not nonsense. No army could advance so fast … and armed with American tanks... Shermans... such speed and fire-power … You are talking out of your belly, because you are frightened … If they could attack us on the road to Baranovici they must have come far …"

"Take no notice," said Mikita, as they reached the edge of the wood and lay down once more in the long grass.

The sun was growing warmer and the shadows that fell across the track on their right which led back to the Stolpcy road were shortening. In a few hours, time the countryside would be shimmering under the midsummer heat and the air would be murmurous with insects. They ate the rations which they had collected on their way and for a time fell silent. There was no longer any sound of gun-fire.

Mikita glanced at his watch, frowned and replaced it in his pocket. It was an old fob-watch which had belonged to his grandfather and he was very proud of it, though he was always mislaying the key. No one in the wood from the second-in-command to the merest trooper appeared to be bestirring themselves unnecessarily. Now and again a voice louder than the others could be heard above the general murmur of conversation and once somebody started to sing, but a torpor seemed to be descending upon everyone as if they were settling again to sleep. It might almost have appeared, thought Sasha, that without Major Shaeffer the battalion would disintegrate as a unit. It was surprising what influence one man, like the Major or Sergeant Karol for that matter, could exert. The little group of officers led by Lieutenant Kubik had returned into the glade where the little stream wended its way to some distant sea, and had sat beside it smoking. They talked at intervals in low undertones and threw pebbles into the stream. Captain Weine stood apart, leaning elegantly against a tree, but he too, like Mikita glanced at his watch from time to time, awaiting the sound of clattering hooves. Under his "plandecke" the second-in-command fumed and swore and sweated, though the heat of the day was not yet on him. It was only half-past six, but the return of the cavalry was now considerably overdue.

Precisely at seven o'clock an ominous and unmistakable rumbling along the Stolpcy road was heard by everyone. It was the sound of tanks.

Sasha and Mikita faced about in their prone position, unperturbed but alert. There had been so many rumours ever since they had begun the retirement on to Minsk that it was the better policy to avoid speculation and accept facts stoically. Nevertheless there was a certain perverted delight in playing the game of make-believe that the worst had happened, because it was equally delightful afterwards to realize it hadn't happened after all. So now Sasha permitted himself the pleasure of a thrill or two down the spine as he told himself that he would pretend that this wasn't another of the familiar panzer columns which of course it was, but a visit from strangers of a far more sinister origin.

"I don't recognize that," said Mikita.

Sasha stole a glance at Mikita who was sitting bolt upright shading his eyes as the rumbling grew nearer. Something was coming slowly along the track in their direction about four hundred yards away and now, attracted by the noise officers and men were emerging from the wood in a casual way such as an idle crowd will always seek diversion.

Mikita's handsome, cheerful face had become set and hard, and there was a little muscle quivering in his jaw-bone as he clenched his teeth. Sasha, a little startled out of his complacent fantasy, crawled to his companion's side.

"What don't you recognize?" he said.

Mikita pointed down the track where the lane began. A large and heavily built tank had come to a standstill and one of the Field Police officers was approaching it.

"It's a Sherman," said Mikita. "That's why we'll never see our cavalry again."

He spoke quietly but with an extraordinary bitterness. The officer was now up by the steel monster. Both friends recognized him as Lieutenant Kubik.

Mikita took Sasha by the arm and his grip was like a vice. His face beneath his tan was so white that his skin looked yellow.

"Oh, the bloody fools!" said Mikita and it sounded as if there was a sob in his throat. "Oh! the bloody, bloody fools," he repeated.

He began to hurry forward in a shambling run, half-dragging the protesting Sasha along with him. He seemed to be trying to call out some kind of warning but nothing but strangulated sounds came out of his throat that ended in incoherent stammering.

They were both now so close to the tank that they could see that its hatch was open and hear what Lieutenant Kubik was saying. There was a renewed rumbling from the main road. Sasha saw two more tanks pass across the junction of the road and lane and then swing lefthanded and disappear from view. It was almost as if an encirclement movement, one of the kind he now knew so well, was being started. Mikita drew up and Sasha stopped beside him. There was no useful purpose to be served in continuing their progress towards the Lieutenant, because it was clearly too late. They could see the Russian markings only too distinctly.

Lieutenant Kubik was talking to someone behind the hatch and was passing his revolver and cartridge-belt in. He was saying:

"Yes, they are all in the wood … an entire battalion … I can only speak for my own platoon, and of course I surrender … if you will let me fetch my company commander …"

He turned on his heel and ran into the wood. The tank's tracks started to grind and she swung slowly round so that her gun covered the path of Kubik's disappearance, and the muzzle began to swing very little from left to right as a hound's nose might snuff a scent.

There was a sudden shouting from the interior of the wood and a blowing of whistles. A horse began to neigh as if it, too, smelt danger. Another tank appeared with the five-pointed star identifications, and came slowly trundling along the lane, bypassing its colleague and heading for the more open track.

"Out of here," said Mikita breathlessly, clutching Sasha's arm once more. "Out of here, before it's too late."

"No!" said Sasha. "We'll stay."

There was a greater horror in feeling that uncouth steel giant fumbling, probing at the small of the back, than even facing it.

"Come on!" yelled Mikita, and his voice sounded womanish and hysterical. He began to run in headlong flight, and for the moment Sasha thought Mikita was about to fling his Smeisser away because he seemed to throw it from him, only the sling prevented it from falling to the ground. Nevertheless he ran on with Sasha at his heels and with the Smeisser thumping against his flank; running on round the wood as if all the hounds of Hades were after him, till he reached on the far side a small hollow in the ground surmounted with branches where he flung himself down, gasping and panting.

Sasha, aghast and horrified at this unexpected display of panic, and acutely conscious that he himself might become infected with it at any moment, despite all his efforts towards self-control, blundered into the brambles, tore himself free, and dropped down beside Mikita. Everything had taken place in so short a space of time, so suddenly, so completely unexpectedly, that he was utterly bewildered and baffled. His heart was thudding in his chest and his lips felt hot and dry as they had after yesterday's long marching; and all the time a part of himself was telling another incredulous part of himself with the utmost conviction that the impossible had taken place, and at the same time assuring himself that even if it had happened, it hadn't happened to him.

It couldn't be true. The retreat had been orderly. He had seen that for himself. They had been falling back — so everybody had kept telling everybody else — on to prepared positions and sooner or later they would face about and make a stand. If the enemy had broken through it could only have been in places and rearguard action would have sealed them off. But where had he heard such stories, such rumours — such lies? He couldn't now at this tremendous and appalling moment pin them down. Perhaps they had never been said at all? Perhaps he had imagined them? Perhaps it was all lies, lies, lies, and the far-flung front line had collapsed and crashed during one hideous night, and there had been no gaps where the enemy had broken through, but the whole line had broken over-powered by one gigantic tidal wave engulfing everything and everybody, sweeping relentlessly, onward to the west.

But it was all happening to him, it was happening to Sasha Nioman of the 34th Field Battalion. It was all happening in seconds, within seconds the whole face of the world was changing. The sunlit July world within a day's march of his own home was changing. He knew what lay in store. They were the legionnaires, the anti-Communists who, according to the enemy should have fought on the Russian side. And now the Russians were here and the battalion was in flight.

He could see them from his hollow in the ground where Mikita lay on his face, shuddering and shaking. He wanted to kick Mikita in the ribs and tell him to get up and look death in the face like a man. Then they could both step forward, hand in hand, and keep their honour like good soldiers, but he couldn't do it if Mikita went on playing the fool, because it destroyed all the courage within himself.

"Pull yourself together, blast you, Mikita," said Sasha, and he knew that his own voice was high-pitched and cracking.

"Damn and blast them," said Mikita. "Damn them all, and all the bloody officers."

"For God's sake pull yourself together," said Sasha. "Put your head up and look over and see what I can see."

It didn't matter if Mikita looked over the edge of the little hollow because there was sufficient to satisfy at least one man's vision.

The battalion was breaking out of the wood. As Sasha watched, a cluster of horsemen gathered at the far end, and for a moment he thought that the cavalry reconnaissance had returned and now, too late, had walked into a trap. Then he saw that the mounted men gathering at the far side were the battalion officers. He could recognize Lieutenant Kubik on the self-same mount to which he himself had been "kutscher." Hauptmann Henkel was there, and he seemed to have fallen off, or his saddle had slipped, because he was clawing at the pommel, hopping on one foot alongside his restive, startled, horse as he attempted to remount. Weine was there and he was already urging his horse into a gallop, digging his heels into its streaming flanks. All the others were there, threading their way out of the wood, and, once in the open, flinging themselves forward on their horses' withers, shaking out the loosened reins on to their horses' necks, urging them forward with whip and voice and spur, so that on the instant they were scattering at full gallop across the countryside. They fled helter-skelter, the Wehrmacht trained officers of the 34th Battalion Field Police, deserting their men in the face of the enemy and leaving them to their fate.

And now the rank and file were beginning to break cover, streaming out of the wood in the wildest disorder, each man bent on saving himself; for the facts had spread like a forest fire and the undisguised, shameless flight of their officers, without whom they were lost, had set its fatal seal upon this dreadful morning.

Beyond the wood a tank began to open fire as the other two originally in the lane appeared round the northern extremity. There was a company of Russian infantry in support of the latter and they were firing from the hip in short bursts as they advanced. Round the lower half of the wood a troop of cavalry appeared, swinging down on the confused crowd of what a quarter of an hour before had been a disciplined battalion. Sasha saw with what superb assurance the horsemen, with their rifles slung across their backs and with their swords drawn, handled their mounts and recognized them for the dreaded Cossacks. Then before he could extricate himself even from his shallow hiding place, the panic-stricken mass of men which had been No. 1 Company was swarming all around him and Mikita, a frantic, confused mob converging, as it were, centripetally as the armour, infantry and galloping cavalry surrounded it.

Not a man of the battalion had fired a shot in self-defence. The tanks — there were six of them in all — took up strategic positions covering the wood while the horsemen and infantry herded the companies together. No one company of the 34th Battalion was to meet another again.

Sasha, struggling to keep his feet in the surging mass, caught sight of Kurt and Symon and fought his way towards them with Mikita in his rear. Someone was shouting in Russian:

"Lay down your arms."

Over the heads of his companions Sasha could see the dark face of the Cossack who gave the order, his mouth a red cavity lined with glittering white teeth beneath his enormous moustache, beneath his rolling eyes.

"Lay down your arms, where you stand."

They laid down their arms. They let them drop upon the ground and then they emptied out their cartridge pouches. The Smeisser slid from Sasha's shoulders and a sob caught in his throat because this was the symbol of his pride and now his pride was nearly all gone — a quarter of an hour of a bright July morning and his honour was stripped from him, and he knew that the end must be very near. But it was not the day nor the weather to die, and the same sort of wild frustrated anger that had filled Mikita and occasioned his outburst at the sight of Lieutenant Kubik surrendering, now filled Sasha, and he bent as if to recover the weapon and redeem himself in his own eyes, but somebody kicked the thing aside and it was lost beneath the trampling feet.

"Now get yourselves into some sort of order and move away to the right."

They obeyed the instructions to the best of their ability. They tried to form up in the usual order and Sasha found himself with his three friends beside him amongst most of the members of No. 1 Platoon.

He wondered then what Sergeant Karol would have done had he been present and not in Radzimichy with Major Shaeffer. Sergeant Karol wouldn't have given up so easily and if the Major had been there, maybe, they would never have been trapped like tamed birds and with never a chance to make a fight of it.

The Russian infantry took over, with the tanks still mounting guard and the Cossacks cantering round in a body. There was comparative quietness, from where the other companies had been segregated, though once or twice a single shot was fired in the vicinity of the Baranovici road and once a great shouting followed by a volley and then silence.

In a little time Sasha could hear renewed movement within the wood and a few minutes later saw the waggons with their harnessed horses emerge on to the lane and then right towards Stolpcy. Russian infantrymen as guards marched at the side of the disarmed drivers with their "kutschers".

At ten o'clock of the morning when the wood was completely empty of all vehicles and horses and men, No. 1 Company was marshalled on the main road. Two tanks remained one at each flank, but the others had departed. There was no sign of the Cossacks and only sufficient of the infantrymen with their tommy-guns remained to form an escort.

The company was now a hundred men strong and each man was searched in turn and his possessions taken from him. Mikita after the initial shock seemed to have regained his nerve because he protested when a guard took the worn photograph of his Davina from his tunic pocket and, grinning, showed it to a companion. The guard, who had a yellowish, hairless face struck Mikita across the mouth with a swinging back-hander and then tore the photograph up.

The order came to march within the hour. They took a secondary road branching off from the main road and in the opposite direction to Radzimichy. It was beginning to grow very hot and the dust rose knee-high. At the tail and in the middle of the column the two tanks rumbled and clanked, and at the head and on either side marched the armed guards. Sasha, Mikita and Symon marched in the same file, Kurt was on the flank of the succeeding file and Josip Polyn stalked along with his indignant head held high two files farther to the rear. On either side of Josip, a Ukrainian, Ales Dubrovnii and Michas Shamso kept pace, while behind them followed three Byelorussians, one whom Sasha had known remotely in Haradischa and the other who was reputed to be in easier times a successful electrical engineer in Baranovici. But whoever they were and where they came from, only one destination now seemed to be assured.

A mile and a half along the road they saw the first dead body of a former member of the battalion. He had been shot in the back, at the base of the skull and his brains lay a spattered puddle in the road. The wound and the method of its infliction reminded Sasha of an execution. They were marching at their regulation pace which was not sufficiently slow to reveal what lay beyond a gap in the hedge which now came into view, just beyond where the corpse lay, but it seemed to Sasha that the hedge had been broken down by the passage of a body of men. Nor could he have sworn that the seeming heaps of tattered rags and a suggestion of upturned boot-heels momentarily glimpsed as they passed by, was anything more than discarded heaps of clothing. Then Mikita whispered hoarsely, close to his ear.

"They are taking no prisoners."

Sasha began to pray under his breath because at last the truth was sinking into him. This was no nightmare however fantastic its qualities, but the solid reality. *They were taking no prisoners.* There had been times before when they themselves had been ordered to take no prisoners. If he remembered rightly there had been one quite notable occasion when he had refused to obey an order of a senior officer to shoot an unarmed man. Was anybody going to refuse to kill him when his time came?

"What will they do with us?" said Sasha.

"Shoot us down like dogs," said Symon on his other side. He was walking steadily forward with an extraordinary look of exaltation on his little, narrow face. He looked as if he were sleep-walking in daylight. Kurt, immediately on Sasha's left rear, growled under his breath:

"We'll make a fight for it. Just give me the chance, and I'll make a fight for it."

"What with?" said Mikita over his shoulder. "Why don't you keep your bloody mouth shut?"

"Silence there!" yelled a guard and swung about with his tommy-gun at the ready and began to elbow his way into the column.

"Who was talking?" he demanded.

The tommy-gun was in Sasha's ribs. He shook his head vigorously and everyone else held their tongue. The guard cursed and shouldered his way out through the files. From ahead a voice called "Halt" and the column concertinaed into itself and stopped. A Russian sergeant came swinging down the line.

"Fall out for five minutes," he said in Russian. "Does anyone know this part of the country? Is there somewhere nearby where we can get a drink of water?"

The two Byelorussians, the one from Dubrova whom Sasha knew, and the Ukrainian, Ales Dubrovnii, stepped forward.

"There's a farm nearby," said the man from Dubrova, "if I remember rightly."

"It will be better for you that you should," said the sergeant.

The man from Dubrova grinned sheepishly as if to acknowledge a very good joke.

"Take that grin off your ugly face," said the sergeant. "And show these other two where your farm is and bring back some water."

Sasha watched them as they passed through a gate and very shortly afterwards a dog started barking. The ground fell away beyond the hedge but on the opposite side of the sheer valley Sasha could see a farm-cart with a driver standing upon it, crossing a field. He was urging his horse forward by flapping the reins against its haunches. Sasha wondered if he knew that his countryside was being invaded and what he would say if he realized that a hundred of his friends were being marched to their death. Then he took a seat beside Kurt while Mikita edged himself nearer to listen more closely.

"Do you think they will kill us?" whispered Sasha.

"I am certain of it," said Kurt.

He spoke quite calmly, in a matter-of-fact tone.

"Do you think they'll do it now?"

"Maybe," said Kurt. "After they've had their drinks."

"Will you make a dash for it, if I do?" said Sasha. "I'm not going to be shot down —" he glanced to where Symon squatted with his back to the bank "like a dog."

Symon never stirred. The same rapt expression was on his face. His lips seemed to be moving very slightly.

"We shouldn't stand a chance at the moment," said Kurt.

"Will you stop that talking!" cried a guard.

He swung his tommy-gun and his dozen companions who were nearby began to move towards their captives. They stopped dead in their tracks as a shot rang out from the valley. There was the distant sound of a man screaming in mortal agony and then another shot. After a long moment's pause a third shot rang out. Thereafter there was silence. One of the Russians began to laugh.

"Missed the first time," he said.

Five minutes later the Ukrainian, Ales Dubrovnii, appeared at the gate. He was staggering under the weight of two brimming buckets of water which slopped over the sides. The sweat was pouring off his forehead and there was a red mark across his cheek as if he had been struck. He put down the two buckets without a word and walked across and joined the others where they squatted on the ground. The guards ladled the water out with their pannikins and one of them went on his knees and lapped it like a cat, from his cupped hand. When they had finished one bucket, not needing the other themselves they kicked it over.

"Fall in," a guard shouted.

One hundred men shuffled their way into ranks. The march began again.

"What happened?" said Mikita, throwing the words over his shoulder.

"There was a Russian officer at the farm," said Ales. "He was a cavalryman because his horse was tied up outside. He was demanding food and drink from the farmer's daughter. When he saw us he looked us all over and then he said to the others: 'You two look the most like Nazis'. Then he shot them both in the stomach. I found two buckets by the pump. It was hard work carrying them full up that hill."

He spoke with regret in his voice, wistfully, as if in recollection of a recent bucketful that could have quenched a clamouring thirst, and Sasha wondered to himself what sense there could be in giving men water however much it might be needed, since in a very little time none of those present might ever thirst again.

The march continued for ten miles. The sun was mounting towards its zenith, and the tanks as they clanked along emitted a smell of oil and petrol and hot iron. Once or twice Sasha caught sight of butterflies by a hedgerow, and a little blue wild flower growing everywhere, but the name of which he had forgotten. Then at a triple cross-roads they were halted.

They jostled into one another, and the tanks lumbered out before them as they were ordered to turn to their front.

There seemed to be something of a concourse on the triangular patch of grass that stood between the juncture of the three roads. There were several horse-drawn waggons with machine-gunners and their weapons ensconced behind the tail-boards, assembled near a platoon of Russian infantry, and literally head and shoulders above them all, sat a giant Cossack officer on a fine, black horse. His lambs-wool, semi-conical hat, was perched at a rakish angle over his eye and his right hand lay clenched upon his thigh, while the reins hung loose on the horse's glossy black neck as it tossed its head and shook its mane to the jingling of the silver bit.

The Cossack, bolt upright in the saddle, stared out over the heads of the men of No. 1 Company and opened his mouth and bawled at them in Russian. He looked what he was, an aristocrat and a conqueror. Maybe, thought Sasha, he is riding back over his own lost lands where his father and his father's father fought for the Czar even before the Communists and their kind were ever even heard of.

"You are now the Prisoners of War of Soviet Russia," he shouted. "You are now the prisoners of the country of which you were a part but which you betrayed. You are traitors to the Red Army, the Fatherland and Communism. You were free to choose, but you preferred to fight for the Nazis and the Swastika. Well, your bed has been made and you will lie in it."

Somewhere inside Sasha a voice was demanding utterance. It wouldn't matter if they shot him where he stood as long as the voice was heard. And the voice was crying out:

"That isn't the truth. We are not Nazis any more than we are Communists, for we hate them both. But we fought for the Germans because they were fighting Communism and *we* were fighting for our independence, for the promised independence of the Ukraine and Byelorussia. That's why we're here and what we stand for."

But the imprisoned voice couldn't find an outlet, and the great Russian mounted on his splendid horse was carrying all before him.

"Strip off your tunics. Take off your caps."

They threw their caps upon the ground, wriggled out of their tunics and kicked them aside. The guards were joined by the infantry platoon who collected the clothing and piled it in heaps by the grass verge. Then the guards and the infantry exchanged roles and the horse-drawn waggons with their gunners took the place of the tanks. Sasha saw that the Russian infantrymen were nearly all elderly men or gangling youths and put them down as third-line reserve troops, brought up to relieve the front line men of work beneath their dignity, beneath, indeed, the menial tasks of leading off, under armed guard, stripped and defenceless prisoners, to a piece of ground allocated for the purpose of execution.

"You will now be marched off," shouted the Cossack officer. "You will march in quick time and with your heads down. There will be no talking. Take 'em away."

He swung his charger round on its hocks and cantered off.

The march continued. The new guards, fresh and eager, urged their jaded prisoners onwards under the guns that dipped from the waggonboards. The heat grew intense as the afternoon advanced. With bowed heads and in silence the prisoner-column trudged along the dusty road. There was much to distinguish them from the once bright lads of the 34th Battalion, Field Police. They marched mechanically, like marionettes, their eyes averted towards the ground. They saw what was becoming a regular sight, the corpses of friends in the other three companies of their battalion.

Where before one corpse had sprawled, now twenty or more lay higgledy-piggledy in a shameless heap; where before some attempt had been made, indifferent though it might have been, to shield the vision of the passer-by from a dreadful business that was deemed necessary, now no effort had been made to disguise what was done in this hideous area. All that remained of the 34th Battalion was being driven to the shambles. And still as in a dream, and unlike the others with his head held high, with enraptured features strode little Symon Ravin.

At the end of the last six miles, despite the vigilance and threatening of the guards, the whisperings began again. There was no doubt in everybody's minds what would happen very soon, though the method of its happening was beyond conjecture.

"I swear to God," said Sasha, "I'll not submit, but I'll go down fighting."

"And I, too," said Kurt.

"When do we break the column?" said Josip Polyn. "We must do it all together."

"All together — yes, altogether," said Michas Shamso, and Mikita nodded.

"Say when, little rascal," said Mikita. "You say 'when' and God have mercy on our souls."

"Silence," cried a guard, dancing on his toes with rage so that his spectacles slipped down the end of the old, thin bridge of his nose.

A rifle butt was swung towards Sasha's face, but he dodged it, throwing his head up. But the movement brought his eyes level with the shoulders of the man before him and over them he caught a fair view of the road ahead so that he saw on either side of it, where it led through a dark and towering wood, a most terrible and horrifying sight.

10

There must have been close on four hundred of them, lining each side of the road, where it led straight and narrow through the high trees and, as yet, gleaming white, with the fine dry dust of midsummer.

They stood silent and waiting, tense and expectant, ready like panthers to spring the moment the signal was given. They were Mongols and Tartars, Cossacks and Russians, of every kind and creed, but all members of the unconquerable Red Army and burning for vengeance and blood. And they were armed with every conceivable kind of weapon from rifles and knives and bludgeons to axes, pickhandles and pistols.

A sort of sigh, an indrawn whispering of anticipation, a licking of the lips so to speak, rose from their ranks as the column of bare-headed, defenceless men approached. They had waited here for this supreme moment, whetting their appetites, since noon. They formed no unit but were drawn as volunteers who could be spared from any contingent on the move in the vicinity. There were cook-house butchers among them and front-line gunners, cavalry-men and mechanics, tank-men and infantry soldiers of several regiments, and they held one object in common, revenge, savage, ruthless and complete. They had been promised a blood-bath, and they were going to have it, wading knee-deep in blood if needs be. It was to be retribution.

They stood quite still grasping their weapons in readiness as the unhappy body of men drew slowly nearer. The machine-gunners secure in their waggons peered through their sights and trained their guns on their victims, but one by one as the column approached the infantry guards began to fall back. It was like driving a company of rats within a wire-pen, but in this instance the wire-walls were composed of armed men.

The head of the column passed within the cuff of the gauntlet, the middle entered, and the tail still wavered as the signal whistle suddenly sounded. With one concerted howl of fury the extermination party fell upon its prey.

They slashed with sabres and lopped off arms and hands; they drove in bayonets with such force and so repeatedly that they stabbed the dead as well as the dying; they hacked flesh with knives and cracked skulls with axes; their yells and whoops of maniacal joy mingled with the screams and curses of the victims, and the snowy-white dust of the midsummer road became a blood-soaked carpet of mud and slime.

Sasha saw Symon Ravin drop to the ground almost completely decapitated by the powerful single sweep of a sword. Mikita staggered and very nearly fell, and as a deafening shot close to Sasha's ear nearly split the drum, he could hear Kurt's voice shouting and seemed to catch sight for one terrible moment of Josip Polyn down on his knees and groping for a knife that had dropped in the sand near the side of the road. Then he himself was leaping across a ditch and someone was at his side, — whether pursuer or pursued he had no time to tell, — with the dark shape of the tall trees before him.

He plunged into the forest. There were still others at his side. From the road behind he could hear the frenzied shouts and still wilder howlings. He ran frantically forward, tripping, stumbling, recovering himself, and blundering on. There were shots ringing out behind, but in what direction they were being fired, he had no conception. He ran on blindly.

He had no idea for how long he ran. Afterwards, piecing it together with the others he decided on half-an-hour, but it could have been twice as long. It was beyond accurate recollection, being beyond time, and limited only by the awful fear that any moment he would feel a steel blade between his shoulders or hear the crash of a pistol being fired at point-blank range. But neither came and he still ran on.

There was little sound now behind him. Even the occasional shot had the whip-crack quality of distance. His knees were sagging beneath him and he felt that his lungs must burst. He drew up to a walk, swayed, and fell against a tree. His hands sought the rough bark, clung there. Figures were flitting between the trees and coming towards him. If they were his pursuers then this must be the end, because he could go no farther. The first of them came into view. It was Mikita.

He was lurching from side to side and his mouth was hanging open in a ridiculous fashion. Then Sasha saw that he was urging along Josip Polyn who was lagging behind. There was a further movement where the trees grew more sparsely and Sasha saw Kurt and Ales Dubrovnii. They were walking and appeared unhurt. He waited till they came up with him.

Mikita stood with hands on his sides, breathing in great gulps. Josip Polyn seemed to have twisted his ankle because he put down a hand and felt the joint gently. They stood panting, fighting for breath. Mikita pointed between the trees and staggered forward. There was a little stagnant pool, miraculously preserved despite the summer heat, in the shade of the forest. The water was foul and soon became muddy in their incautious haste, but they knelt on their hands and knees like animals, or lay on their faces with their mouths immersed. Very soon the water had sunk low and was too thick to drink, but they had had their fill and sat back.

"Symon's killed," said Mikita and wiped his mud-stained lips with the back of his hand. "I saw him go."

"I think they were all killed — the others," said Kurt. "How could any escape? We were lucky."

"For the moment —" said Josip, and began to scramble to his feet. Alarmed, the others followed suit. There was a movement some way off amongst the trees, a fluttering grey whiteness as of a man in shirt sleeves running. He was coming towards them with long but faltering strides. Then Sasha saw it was Michas Shamso.

His fair hair was plastered over his forehead and there was an ugly cut down his forearm as if from a knife, and the blood had run down past his wrist and was dripping at his finger-tips. He paused for a moment to recover his breath and then began, since he was still breathless, to jab a finger in the direction whence he had come. Sasha gestured with his forearm and the party set off again. Nobody seemed to dispute Sasha's right to take the lead. The pursuit was still on.

There was no sound at all from behind, though they knew that might be of little significance. The forest seemed to be thinning out a little on their right and they began to walk and made their way to where the sky showed through the tree-tops. Sasha held up a finger for caution and they went forward more slowly, keeping close together, a little huddled group of six jacketless, unarmed men, without caps or insignia of what once had been a disciplined unit. With their mud-stained, dusty clothes they could have been taken for a band of gypsies — or Partisans!

As the trees began to open out they caught the first glimpses of the road and heard the sound of an approaching vehicle. With one accord they doubled on their tracks and plunged once more into the denser part of the wood. And now from their right as if suspicions had been aroused, came the sound of a lorry coming to a standstill, and then not seventy yards away a faint murmur of voices in Russian followed by a crackling of dry undergrowth. Seized with renewed panic the little party resumed their flight.

But now though the fear raced through their veins and into their feet, each had recovered sufficient control to use a brain quickened and not paralyzed by terror. They knew what they wanted and instinctively sought for it. Their need was cover.

They found the thorn thicket where the forest stopped short at a clearing. The thorn was fully seven feet high in places and it spread some forty yards each way over a glade encircled with the tall trunks. Somewhere in the distant recesses of the wood a shot suddenly rang out and a moment later from where they imagined that they had left the road, came a distant shouting. Without further hesitation the six fugitives struggled into the brambles on hands and knees.

The thorns caught at their shirts and tore small shreds from them, the brambles scored their limbs, but somewhere nearby they knew the enemy were searching because they could hear them calling to one another and sometimes the voices grew shriller with a sudden excitement as if a trail or a foot-print had been discovered. Therefore, regardless of the torment of thorn and tangle they pressed on crawling close to the ground and hoping the scraps of their clothing which they left behind them would not betray their presence and direct burst after burst of tommy-gun fire in their wake.

Once the voices grew very near and somebody seemed to be beating the bushes round the perimeter of their hiding place so that Sasha expected a volley every moment to smash through the undergrowth, but none came, and with the dusk there was silence.

He lay in the little nest he had scooped out by the side of Kurt. Every time he stirred a barb stabbed him, and in places the scratches were beginning to set up an intense irritation, but it could still be fatal to indulge in anything but the smallest of movements. After over an hour of silence they ventured to speak in whispers.

"I would give my soul for a mouthful of water," said Kurt.

"And I for a loaf of bread," said Sasha.

"Do you think we should remain here?" asked Kurt.

Sasha, astonished that this all-knowledgeable young man who had fought before Stalingrad should seek advice other than his own, fell silent for the moment. Then he said:

"Yes. We've got to be absolutely certain there's no one around when we break cover."

"I think that's right," said Kurt. Then after a little time he said:

"I am sorry about Symon Ravin. I misjudged him, but then he disliked me. Nevertheless I am sorry."

"He has been ill for a long time," said Sasha. "Ill in the head, I would say. It has been coming on for months."

"What are your plans?" said Kurt. "You know more about this kind of fighting than I do. It is very different from Stalingrad."

"I think we ought to lie up for a day to let the countryside settle down."

"Very well," said Kurt. "That is what we will do then."

Towards midnight the traffic on the nearby road began to increase. The sound of the Russian advance had been spreading over the entire area in the last two hours, as the roads became congested with convoys and armoured columns. The speed of the advance was such that it savoured of a complete break-through and collapse, or a hurried retreat to evade encirclement in the face of an enemy who completely held the initiative. But just after midnight the Luftwaffe came in, on the counter-attack.

The first bombs fell wide of the mark and into the forest. The detonations shook the ground beneath the fugitives, but their hearts exulted. As the salvos began to drop more regularly with each stick of exploding bombs, Sasha and his friends took courage and found themselves calling out in bravado from their hiding-place words of encouragement. But at dawn the Luftwaffe withdrew and the sounds from the neighbouring road once more increased.

At dusk of the following day, during a lull in the traffic, they managed to cross the road to the forest opposite, darting across one by one. None had taken food nor drink for nearly thirty hours. Once deep within the close-set wood, they gathered in a circle round Sasha. He was impressed to find himself in the centre.

"What's our plan?" said Josip Polyn. "We ought to agree on one. What do you think, Sasha? This is more your home country than mine, and you know the lie of the land."

"We must find the Wehrmacht," said Sasha, "and join with them again."

"Or," said Mikita, "We could disperse and each go our own way. We stand a better chance on our own."

"We must stay together," said Kurt.

"Have it your own way," said Mikita sourly. "I'm not a bloody regular —".

"Enough of that!" said Kurt.

"If we're to get out of this with a whole skin," said Sasha, "We've got to keep our tempers as well as our heads."

It surprised nobody, least of all Sasha himself, that he had assumed his newly and suddenly acquired mantle of authority with such unconscious ease.

11

This then was their plan; they would forge ahead as rapidly as possible and overtake the retreating German armies. Then when the time came, as it assuredly must, for the Wehrmacht to turn and make their stand, they themselves would be once again in their rightful place in the company of their comrades-in-arms. For despite the massacre of the 34th Battalion there was, they assured themselves, no indication that the German armies as a whole were in desperate plight.

If during the first night's vigil in the thorn thicket the retreat had sounded as if it were widespread, then they argued that such an impression was born of their own deplorable circumstances. Now, with their first panic evaporated, and with the fact that they had contrived to escape even so far, their spirits rose. They set their faces to the west, and since it was agreed that he knew the country best, Sasha led the way and none disputed him.

The forest seemed endless. Bareheaded, clad only in shirt and trousers, they flitted like ghosts amidst the trees. At times the undergrowth rose waist-high and grew in great patches, but at other times their path was made easy with moss and dry earth beneath their feet. Water they found in plenty from the occasional streams which they encountered, but they had begun to draw in their belts by midnight of the second day. Then for the first time for nearly forty-eight hours they suddenly heard the sound of horses and voices other than their own. The voices were speaking in Byelorussian.

Josip Polyn who was walking at the time by Sasha's side, started forward at the sound, but Sasha caught him by the arm restraining him. The other four, close on their leader's heels rapidly approached. The little group clustered together listening intently.

Someone was passing nearby and from the comparative silence of the horses' hooves it was apparent that a track rather than a road was unexpectedly crossing their path some few yards ahead. Sasha and Josip crept forward on hands and knees while the rest remained under cover of a fallen tree. The moon was up, full and brilliant, and stood high above the glade.

A party of mounted men were coming down the open path towards them. They could see that the party was armed because the moonlight gleamed on the metal components and muzzles of the rifles slung across their shoulders. From the long manes and tails of the horses and the peaked caps of the leading file Sasha would have judged them to be Cossacks but for the fact that they were speaking in his own tongue. For the moment a wild hope filled his mind that they might be some obscure cavalry unit an organization similar to the Field Police and he was about to make himself known when he heard the leader speak.

He was riding a few paces ahead of the troop and he turned in the saddle to address the man riding behind him.

"I shall take the road, to Niesviz when I get south of Stolpcy," he said. "The area should, be clear of the enemy by then."

Both towns, as Sasha knew only too well were now in Russian hands. He motioned to Josip to he low while he himself edged back into the pitch black shadow of the wall of trees. Seconds later the first of the horses passed by and he could have struck it on the haunch with the flat of his hand. When the last had trotted past he made his way back with Josip to where the others waited. The sound of the horsemen's voices could still be heard down the warm night air.

"Partisans," said Sasha and the others saw him, caught in a moonray, grinning with relief. Then when the world was quiet again with a stillness almost of the tomb, they crossed the glade lit by the moon and stepped into the sheltering trees on the other side.

They walked on till first light, and saw the moon slant down the sky till it became entangled in the mid-branches of the forest and the dawn come up on its hem. The first grey light came out of the east and they tightened their belts again. And then of a sudden with a thinning of the trees, as daylight comes to waking eyes, the forest ended.

The six of them stood at the forest's edge overlooking the meadowed countryside beyond. It was going to be another hot day, because again there was a blanket of mist on the ground and only the tops of the hedges could be seen; but farther on homesteads were visible.

"When the mist clears," said Sasha, "One of us will go down to that farm and ask for bread."

The choice fell on Michas Shamso and he made his way across the fields within the hour. The remainder sat down to wait but Sasha withdrew a little from the others because the memory of another such morning was with him and he was fearful of betraying his thoughts. Then, at the break of another dawn he had emerged from a similar dark and gloomy wood and had stood upon a hill and faced a new day with joy and pride in his heart, because he had found his manhood. Then his comrades had been around him in their scores, confident and jubilant. Now where were they? Slaughtered in heaps along the sandy lanes round Stolpcy.

He glanced across to where Mikita and Josip sat with their backs to a tree and Kurt and Ales Dubrovnii lay beside them face downwards to the ground with their heads in the crook of their arms. Nobody appeared to be talking and he wondered if they too were busy with their bitter thoughts. It was the first time they had seemed to be able to relax since their flight through the forest after the happenings of that hideous Sunday afternoon.

One by one he looked them over, and he thought what a very short time was needed to turn smart soldiers into such a scarecrow crew. The branches had played havoc with their garments; one sleeve had nearly been ripped from Mikita's shirt and his knee was already through his trousers, Josip's chest was practically bare and scored with scratches, and Kurt's shirt was split down the back while Ales' underpants were revealed through a gigantic tear in his seat. If they looked like this within a week he wondered what a month might do to them. Already they were completely unshaven, unwashed and bedraggled.

A month? There was no reason why he should have specified any length of time. A month was a century away. By that time anything might happen. He almost shuddered to think what could befall any of them; and now they were turning to him as a leader. When he thought of that a great emptiness seemed to take the place of his stomach and he found himself calling with that inner voice for Nicola. When he realized that now Nicola would probably never come again, he was calling, surprisingly, for Sergeant Karol. Then he suddenly saw Michas returning across the meadow and went down to meet him.

Michas was carrying a loaf. Sasha recognized it for what it was five yards away, and saw that it was untouched. That, he thought, was characteristic of Michas who always seemed to think of himself last.

"You've had luck," said Sasha, when he reached him.

They stood knee high in the lush long grass that now might never be mown for hay but beaten down with tank-treads and trampling horses. Michas smiled his wonderful smile that not even his grimy face could disguise.

"I had the greatest difficulty," said Michas. "They barred the door on me at first sight. They took me for a Partisan."

"You told them who you were?"

"I think that made it worse. Sasha, I think every man's hand is against us now. We are nobody's children." He glanced up shyly at Sasha. "Except, perhaps, God's," he said.

They walked in silence to the forest, and arrived there Michas did his best to break the loaf into six equal parts. They sat in the shade and ate slowly to the last crumb. The sun was mounting steadily and the sky was cloudless.

"I think we will make in the direction of Baranovici," said Sasha. "It's about forty miles off. What do you say?"

"It should be on the line of retreat," said Kurt.

"I stay here," said Mikita suddenly.

He looked defiantly from one to another. All but he had risen to their feet.

"Stay here!" said Josip. "They'll soon catch up with you and make mince-meat of you."

"I can look after myself," said Mikita sourly. He turned to Sasha.

"Go on your way, little rascal," he said. "There is a village near here where my uncle has a farm. He will take me in and I shall hide there."

"You!" said Kurt. "A deserter!"

"You can call me what you like," said Mikita. "But I have been thinking. All along there has been too much foolish talk altogether, right from the beginning there has been promises and foolish talk. What did the Germans say to us but that when the war was won we should have our independence. It's a good way to win a war by running away."

"I am a German and a soldier —" began Kurt.

"You are a Nazi and a bloody fool," said Mikita.

He held up a warning hand.

"No, keep your distance. I am just as strong as you, Kurt Hermann, and if you have any sense left in that bullet-head of yours you will know I am speaking the truth. You are not one of us. We are not Nazis any more than we are Communists, and for all I see both are tarred with the same brush that stinks. We are the legionnaires, the dead ones and the damned, my boy, who fight for the side who will reward us with our rights — our independence. Well — *bah!*"

He spat on the ground beside him.

"Bah! We should have known better. After two hundred years of this sort of monkey-business shouldn't we have refused to be made fools of again? No, not us. It's the same old bait and we rise to it, gobble, gobble, gobble. It makes me sick. Well, I will tell you this. The best view I have had of a highborn Wehrmacht regular officer is the split-arse backside view of your Lieutenant Kubik as seen from astern bent half out of his saddle with the Red Army hot on his tail."

"Get up," said Kurt, deadly white to his lips under his grime. "Get up —"

"Oh! I'll get up," said Mikita. "Else you'll be up to your Gestapo tricks and begin kicking me up —"

He lumbered to his feet and both men were locked together before any of the others could intervene. They swayed and struggled together, grunting and groaning with their efforts, until Mikita with a mighty heave broke free, and swung his fist to send it smashing into Kurt's face.

Kurt fell back with a gasp and before he could start forward Sasha and Josip had seized his arms while Michas and Ales stood between the antagonists.

"Let me get at him," cried Kurt, struggling to free himself.

"Don't be such a bloody fool," said Josip. "Do you want the countryside about our ears?"

Mikita took a couple of steps back towards the tree against which he had been sitting, but now on his feet he leant against it, his hands thrust deep into his trouser pockets and a truculent, scornful look on his face.

"You go on your way, little rascal." And he was doubtless speaking to Sasha. "On your way, little rascal, on your way. And it's a damned hard thing for me to have to say, who like you well enough. But friends must part when opinions clash and I've had enough of fighting other people's battles, and getting kicked in the crutch for my trouble. So off you go and good luck to you, little rascal, and never say die."

Sasha wanted to make the appropriate reply. He should have repeated the phrase as had been their custom, but the words stuck in his throat and his sight wasn't as good as it should have been because there were hot and angry tears smarting in his eyes. Therefore he clawed Kurt's shoulder round while Josip slipped an arm through the bend of his elbow in an armlock. He lugged at Kurt's shoulder and between them they half-carried, half-dragged, Kurt out of the forest, with Ales and Michas bringing up the rear. Then still keeping control of the young Nazi, they began to make their way along the edge of the meadow.

Back in the wood Mikita stood by the tall tree and his customary gay and handsome features were drawn and haggard, and there was a grey look under his skin, as if the brief encounter with Kurt had exhausted him, which it could not possibly have done. Quite suddenly he turned to face the tree and remained in that position for a considerable time, with his forearm propped against the trunk and his forehead on his arms. At last he turned and with a great shuddering sigh drew himself up to his full height, and then with long, swinging strides and with the ripped sleeve of his shirt fluttering from his shoulder like a banner, stepped out into the early morning sunshine, making his way in the direction opposite to that Sasha and his party had taken.

A mile and a half farther on from the summit of a hillock Sasha saw the second farmstead. It lay in a little hollow with trees around it. There was a wisp of grey smoke rising from a chimney and all around the countryside breathed and blossomed like a flower. The morning was still cloudless and nowhere was there any indication that a fierce and cruel war was in progress. There was occasional movement amongst the trees in the distant dell and Sasha determined now to investigate himself. He was, moreover, perturbed at Michas's news of his reception on the previous occasion. It was going to prove awkward if even their friends failed to recognize who they were.

He found the farmer and his young wife mucking down the pig-sty. They had let the old sow out in the orchard and she was rooting at the boles of the trees while the piglets squealed and scampered around her. When she lay down with a thump and rolled over on her side they charged at her belly and butted at her udder, scrambling over one another in their eagerness to reach her. The farmer, who was tall and lean with strong, white teeth and a sharp blue eye, looked Sasha over with suspicion at first but became friendly when Sasha explained that he was from Radzimichy and that his own father farmed at the village of Dubrova. The farmer's wife had friends in Radzimichy and her family as well had been divided by the war, with an elder sister nursing for the Germans and a younger brother fighting with the Partisans.

The wife gave Sasha a parcel of food and the husband some words of advice.

"Move away from this district towards the west as soon as you can. We've not seen much trouble here and don't want to, but there are rumours, of course, and we have heard the gunfire and the bombing at night. Nobody seems to know just how far off the Russians may be, but parties of them have been seen close by. The last of the Germans passed through here thirty-six hours ago but stragglers have been coming in ever since. Nobody seems to know quite what's happening except that the Russians are still advancing and the Germans are in retreat."

Sasha thanked the farmer for the information and turned to go, but the wife's curiosity had been whetted and she asked how Sasha came to be in such a plight and he told her of the massacre and its aftermath. She grew very indignant and was shocked by the story, but the farmer said:

"I don't know rightly that we should have helped you after all seeing who were your allies."

"My brother is a Partisan," said Sasha as if that equalized matters, but the farmer continued to shake his head and Sasha wondered if he would demand the food back.

"Does it matter who he is, the poor boy," said the young wife, and her eyes filled with tears. "Whatever side he was on there would be plenty to say it was the wrong one. And you say you lived at Dubrova?"

"Yes, ma'am," said Sasha. "We had a farm like yours. There was an orchard too and we kept pigs. Then they came one night and stole our pig, they shot the old sow, and carried off my brother Nicola —" He broke off short and bit his lip.

"You could stay with us," said the young wife.

The farmer shook his head vigorously but she took no notice of him.

"Oh! yes he could," she said. "We could hide him and then when things quietened down he could help us work the farm. I think it's a fine idea."

"And get shot by the Russians for harbouring a German deserter. No, thank you."

"He is not a German. Are you?" she said. "He's a Byelorussian and that's nobody's concern, there are as many on one side as the other and many more who are on nobody's side at all. Wouldn't you like to stay with us?"

"Nobody's concern," repeated Sasha. "That's what Mikita said."

"Who's Mikita?" she demanded.

"My friend who was with us but left us to do what you are suggesting I should do. May I keep the food, please, sir?" he asked the farmer.

"Of course," said the farmer. "Keep the food by all means but don't take no notice of a woman's tongue that talks too easily."

The young wife stamped her foot.

"It is a splendid scheme and it would work. Wouldn't you rather be here with us," she asked Sasha, "than risking all manner of dangers?"

"Indeed I would —" he began.

"There!" she cried. "What did I tell you!"

"But it can't be done," said Sasha.

The old sow heaved herself to her feet and the piglets still butted and pummelled her as she struggled up. There was a hive at the bottom of the orchard and the buzzing of the bees was in the warm and scented air. A lurcher dog had joined the group of three and was snuffling at Sasha's legs. Then it suddenly leapt up as if its nose had confirmed its instinct, and its front paws were at his belt and it was licking his hand. He stroked the creature's head and it dropped away from his side and retreated foot by foot on crouched and outspread forelegs, barking invitation. From somewhere nearby a horse neighed.

"Why can't it be done?" said the young wife.

"I have four friends waiting for me up the hill," said Sasha, "And they expect me to return to them and now I must go, ma'am, if you please, but thank you with all my heart."

He climbed the incline between the trees and out of the dell. He carried with him a picture in his mind of the farmer's young wife with her flushed cheeks and gleaming, misty eyes that promised adventure, but still more clearly he carried a memory of another orchard and another homestead from which he was now utterly debarred. Now more than ever he must refuse to return home for with the coming of the Russians combined with his own recent activities, the peril to his family would be doubled. And if the Germans once again drove the Russians back still more untenable would be his position as a deserter. A few short weeks and the face of his world had altered beyond recognition. He was no longer a victorious soldier but a bedraggled and discredited fugitive. He was an outcast in his native land; an outcast, spumed of man and spurned of God, one for whom there was no place at all to lay his head. When he reached the hillock where the others waited, Kurt cried out:

"What a time you've been. I thought maybe you'd followed your friend Mikita's example. You, too, are near home."

"Or, much more likely," said Josip Polyn shrewdly, "stopped to investigate an offer."

"He's brought some food with him," said Michas, who almost unfailingly seemed to know when to come to the rescue.

12

It was one thing to make a plan, another to carry it out. It was all very well to decide to rejoin the German Army as loyal allies but it was essential to discover the whereabouts of the army, if that purpose were to be achieved successfully. But it was now mid-afternoon with their meal a memory, and there was nothing on land or in the sky that remotely suggested war, much less the Wehrmacht.

The heat beat down on their backs and the pollen lay thick on their boots. To the best of Sasha's knowledge and ability they had kept the course for Baranovici, which was under fifty miles due west of Stolpcy and through where the German columns might be retreating. On the other hand the supposition might be hopelessly incorrect, because anything could be happening.

But it was comforting to have a plan so they marched on confidently. Their spirits rose. They even joked, and for an interval they sang in the sort of soldier unison that goes for a marching song. It was a good old, senseless jingle that had always been a favourite with the battalion and it seemed to put new heart into the five survivors.

> "*I caught my bandit at the end of the wood,*
> "*Jigger-jig, young man, jigger-jig,*
> "*I strung him up both hard and good,*
> "*Jigger-jig, young man, jigger-jig.*"

As the afternoon deepened they grew hungry again, but they had reached open, rolling country which seemed bereft of farms or other dwelling houses. Several separate roads swept over the broad shoulders of the downs and at times they could see three or four miles at a stretch, but there was curiously little traffic upon them. It was as if the former congestion of lorries nose to tail-board, ammunition waggons, armoured vehicles, and panzers had never been. This was the countryside as Sasha had so often known it, quiet and peaceful.

About six o'clock they climbed a low hill with the ghost of a grassy track running across it. It could have been one of those point-to-point routes of the ancient wandering peoples of whose habitations and camping grounds no traces now remained. The track passed through a col at the southern extremity of the shoulder of a small ridge. By the time the five survivors had reached the summit they considered they needed rest.

They flung themselves down on the sun-dried grass just beneath the crest. Down below them the dust-white ribbon of a road was looped into the shallow valley and over the slow rise in the ground. There was not a sign of human activity along it.

"How much farther to Baranovici?" said Michas.

"About twenty-five miles," said Sasha. "It'll be the same distance to the south as Radzimichy is to the north."

The westering sun cast the shadow of the low ridge along the crest across the grass beside them. It made a hard, distinct outline that, as the minutes progressed towards dusk, would creep downhill.

"I don't believe he knows where he is," said Josip Polyn. "I think he makes it all up. Just because —"

He broke off short, staring at the ground before him almost incredulously, and the remainder following his look saw what Josip saw — the silhouette in shadow of a man's head appearing over the little ridge behind them. As they watched, it disappeared as silently and mysteriously as it had risen.

All five stared at one another with surprise upon their faces. There had been no sign of any human being other than themselves, certainly for the last couple of hours. They made no move but waited. There was no sound from over the ridge nor repetition of that tell-tale shadow. Kurt gestured with his hand for silence and rose cautiously to his hands and knees; then he started to crawl towards the ridge. As he began to ascend the slope, the others closed in behind him.

Someone had been observing them for several seconds while Sasha had been answering Michas's question. That was quite clear and it was somebody who had no intention of introducing himself. It could be an enemy or equally it could be a friend. Sasha sat down stolidly on the grass because in his opinion Kurt's action in determining to stalk their eavesdropper suddenly appeared to be foolish and melodramatic. Nevertheless he refrained from rising to his feet till Kurt had gained the top of the ridge and was beckoning them all forward, then he covered the intervening dozen yards and was beside Kurt and looking over and down with the others into the sunken track that ran parallel to the crest.

There was nobody immediately below them, but a man was running down the track, along to the left. And the man was in uniform. Then beyond the runner they saw, seated on either side of the track where it narrowed almost to the width and depth of a broad ditch, score upon score of armed men.

Some were squatting on their haunches, others lying on their backs, some sprawled face downwards and a few stood chatting. They could not have been more than a quarter of a mile off, two or more companies of infantry soldiers resting; and the colour of their uniform was field-grey. Even as Sasha watched he saw the runner reach the first of them, and point in the direction of himself and his companions.

Kurt rose boldly to his feet, standing on the skyline in full view of those beneath.

"At last! This is what we've been looking for," he said. "They are German soldiers. We have found the Wehrmacht. Leave it to me. I'll go down and make myself known to them as none of you speak our language. When I call you, follow me on down."

He set off at a brisk pace, producing a grimy handkerchief from his trouser pocket which he proceeded to wave frantically from time to time. It was, Sasha supposed, just as well to take such precautions because he could see how one or two of the recumbent men had sat up and grabbed their rifles. For all its apparent peacefulness this was indeed a countryside where sudden death could lurk. Nevertheless, there was something comic in the spectacle of Kurt, half stumbling in his eagerness at each downhill step, and with his improvised flag of truce fluttering at arm's length, so that Sasha burst out laughing, knowing as he did so that it was as much from relief as it might be from mirth, because those below were the long-sought Wehrmacht and would prove to be friends.

Kurt had reached them by now and was talking animatedly, and pointing up the hill. There were several men around him listening attentively, and others were approaching and joining the group. One of them, who appeared to be somebody in authority was shouldering his way through the little crowd towards Kurt. Then there was more gesticulating and pointing till Kurt cupped his mouth with a hand and shouted. The four of them began to run down the slope as he came to meet them.

They met some fifty yards from the Germans. Sasha felt like singing for joy, for this was all they could have desired. They were adrift no longer; here was some form of anchorage where they could find their proper place in an ordered and familiar organization. Very soon he would have a rifle back on his shoulder and a cap and uniform to wear. He felt painfully undressed to the point of nakedness with so many decently clad men at hand.

But Kurt looked grave, and there was that disagreeable droop to the corners of his mouth which he affected when displeased.

"I've told them all about us," he said. "They're part of the 78th Division of the Fourth Army that was cut up by General Rokossovsky. They seem to have been lucky to get away." Then he added, "They don't want anything to do with us."

"What's that?" said Ales. His honest, simple face was filled with dismay.

"Not want us?" echoed Sasha.

Josip Polyn glanced down at his mud-stained trousers and torn shirt.

"No wonder," he said. "What could they take us for anyway?"

"I did my best," said Kurt. "But when they asked me to identify myself and my friends — What could I do? I could only repeat what had happened."

"Didn't they believe you?" said Sasha.

"I don't know whether they did or whether they didn't, but they weren't going to take the risk of finding they were associating with Partisans or their own deserters and they said as much. The fact that we were their allies didn't seem to count for much. We're not the Wehrmacht."

As if to confirm Kurt's words a dozen or more soldiers were coming rapidly along the track towards them. Sasha could see that at least two of them had been wounded in the recent fighting because one carried his left hand in a sling and another was wearing a bandage round his head. They were gesticulating menacingly as they approached, and one was flapping his hands as a countryman would shoo away a flock of geese.

"Come on," said Kurt. "We'd better be off."

He turned as if to go, but Sasha caught him by the shoulder.

"This isn't good enough," he said. "Make them understand, Kurt. We're their allies, we're on their side."

"They won't believe you," said Kurt. "They would have taken me with them, because I speak German and that convinced them, but they won't take a risk with you or the others. See for yourself."

They were surrounded now and there was no mistaking the hostile attitude of the soldiers. One of them, a tall broad-shouldered youth with a little dark Hitler moustache who stood inches above the remainder was the first to reach the bedraggled and tattered little group. Without more ado he swung Michas round and brought the butt of his rifle to the tail of his spine. It was not a violent blow, but it was indicative of what might follow, because when Michas faced about and put up his fists two more of them hustled him around again in the opposite direction and sent him spinning. Then with the Germans closely following them Sasha's party reached the top of the ridge once more and began to descend the other side. It was not until they arrived at the bottom of the slope that the line of heads watching from the crest disappeared from view. Then in silence, with no song now on their lips, the fugitives retraced their footsteps across the valley till they could resume their course for Baranovici. But the incident had occupied more than an hour, and now the sun was dropping behind the horizon and the light beginning to leave the sky.

"And now what is our plan?" said Josip Polyn. He drew in his belt and spat on the ground.

"To find our own people," said Sasha.

"I can think of nothing easier," said Josip Polyn, sarcastically. "How's your backside, Michas? If thine enemy smite thee on one cheek, then offer him the other."

They walked on through the night, resting at intervals and when they went on again it was with caution. The open country was growing more close-set and there seemed to be more frequent wooded areas which Sasha only vaguely remembered, if at all. But the night was fine and warm and by midnight the moon was up, and in the early hours of the morning they came across a farm and decided to explore the immediate environs for a barn where they could he up till morning. But a barking and persistent dog forced them to change their plans once more; and since in broad daylight it seemed they could find no friends then in the darkness all would be enemies, so they moved on and finding a road, walked a mile along it, and climbed into a field and sat against the hedge. The moon was beginning to fade and they were becoming hungry again.

They sat for a long time in silence because they were feeling low with every man's hand against them though each one knew that a turn in their luck and their spirits would soar again. Once Ales in his guileless fashion advanced an opinion that seemed to be general.

"I expect that Kurt is regretting," said Ales, "His decision not to join the Germans. Aren't you Kurt?"

Kurt grunted "Maybe."

"In one way," said Josip Polyn, "You were a bit of a fool weren't you, Kurt?"

"Maybe," said Kurt.

"Just as much of a fool as Sasha was to return to us when we waited for him on the top of a hill," said Michas. "When he need not have done."

"I said 'in one way'," said Josip Polyn.

Their misfortunes were fast cementing their comradeship.

At dawn they saw that they were on the outskirts of a village and congratulated themselves that they had not blundered into it in the dark and risked further misunderstandings. It lay on the main road to Baranovici and Sasha remembered it by the name of Volna. He dismissed the place from his mind beyond the fact that it was to be avoided. They had no wish for a repetition of yesterday evening and the kind of reception they had received. Now more than ever they would hold their hand until they were certain that they had found their own people.

Therefore they took a bridle path crossing a meadow on which the houses of the main street backed with their vegetable gardens and chicken runs. There appeared to be nobody about at that hour and only an occasional chimney was smoking. Now and again from the far side of the line of dwelling houses they could hear the rumble of lorries and the whine of changing gears so that they wondered if the dawn convoys were going through again, and that if they had encountered once more the main stream of heavy traffic flowing steadily westwards. But they had no inclination to poke their noses into trouble by investigating unnecessarily, and plodded across the field intent on skirting Volna and any over-inquisitive persons it might contain. Very soon the bridle path passed through a coppice then swung abruptly to the right, where Sasha fancied it would meet the main road and then all would be well.

As they trailed out of the little wood into the open they knew that all was very far from being well and that the trap had closed with so sharp a snap that there was never a chance to spring clear. Three fully armed members of the German Military Police, walking abreast, came striding down upon them. When they turned in their tracks there were two more emerging from amongst the trees by the very path which they themselves had just taken.

They put up their hands at the first curt command of the sergeant while two private soldiers ran expert fingers over their tattered shirts and down their torn trousers as if indeed any weapon could have been concealed there. All the time Kurt kept explaining and emphasizing points in his fluent German with a pounding of the palm of one hand with the clenched fist of the other, which in the end brought him a cuff on the ear that sent him staggering. After that it seemed better to Kurt that he should hold his tongue, though he kept muttering to himself and complaining. Then they were marched into Volna.

The traffic was streaming through the village. The distant tide of battle flowing more urgently every hour and rising like a flood, was jamming the main-roads, and then like a river in spate, piling up on itself ton by ton, only suddenly to spew forth in a chaotic deluge of vehicles. But though by the time it reached Volna the torrent had lost something of its impact and speed, nevertheless the solid phalanx of metal and armour was awe-inspiring, and in the rapidly warming air the reek of diesel oil and petrol was overpowering.

Kurt tried once more to explain and to identify themselves when they reached the tiny market square and were halted there. Sasha and the other three, not understanding a word of what was said, could only glance with eagerness combined with apprehension from the stern faces of their captors to that of Kurt, protesting and pleading.

It was all in vain. They were given a brief and hurried meal and they were one by one ignominiously bundled over the tailboard of a lorry, which in turn was edged into the main stream of traffic and set on its way.

"And what," said Josip Polyn, "may be the outcome of all this pleasant conversation with our handsome allies. Do we get shot?"

"Not yet," said Kurt sourly.

"That's very comforting," said Josip.

"It's the same old thing," said Kurt. "We're either deserters or Partisans. They can't — or won't — identify us."

So this, thought Sasha, was the outcome of all their tribulations and efforts. He sat on the floor of the lorry with the petrol fumes rising through the floor-boards as they progressed head to tail in the endless procession of vehicles. Immediately behind them a ten ton lorry was loaded with ammunition in cases and ahead an open truck contained a "gruppe" of infantry. Every now and again, in the one-way traffic, another smaller truck containing soldiers would range up alongside as if attempting to pass, only to fall back at the shouts of an overworked outrider on a motor-bicycle who with scores of his colleagues patrolled fretfully along the flanks of the cortege. Someone in the little lorry had availed himself of several bottles of vodka and the occupants were taking their fill. Once as they drew level Sasha essayed a wan smile at a sturdy drinker with his steel helmet pushed well to the back of his head but all he received in return was a scowl and a glare, and as the vehicle fell back he saw the man dig his elbow into his neighbour's ribs to attract his attention, and saw the latter leaning out over the side and for some astonishing reason shaking his fist. Thereafter he made no further friendly overtures in any direction, but sat swaying or jogging in the give-and-take of the lurch and jolt of the lorry, with his elbows on his knees and his chin on his hands.

His thoughts were bitter. Kurt had asked the two guards who accompanied them where they were bound for and what was likely to be in store for them and had received in reply that they were on their way to Stalavichi where they would be interrogated. As for their future it depended on what the Intelligence Officer who was to do the questioning found out about them. Any further attempts on Kurt's part to draw the guards met with cold and contemptuous indifference and the conversation lapsed. But it was news to Sasha. Mamma had been born a mile from Stalavichi. She had often spoken of the place when she had been alive, and several times too, Papa in later life had visited there because Mamma had relations nearby. Little could she have imagined in those far off dead days that her own flesh and blood who had not then been born, would travel to that self-same place half-stripped and looking like a vagabond.

Because that was what he was, a vagabond, a homeless wanderer, denied by his own kind. The bitter thoughts welled up inside him. Mamma was gone and well out of it too, God rest her soul. But where was Papa and Valia, Nicola and Walter? What dark forest or still darker grave concealed Nicola? Were the others, only in truth a hand's breadth away, still in the farm at Dubrova near the county town of Radzimichy which had once been his proud battalion headquarters?

Once he had possessed a rifle; and now it had been taken from him. Always it seemed there had been a rifle at the back of everything. It had been a rifle that had prompted the quarrel with Ivan Zavada. It was a rifle he had striven for when he had led Lieutenant Kubik's horse as a "kutscher." It was a rifle he had gained under the glinting, mocking eyes of Sergeant Karol. It was from a rifle he had been promoted to a Spandau — and now, oh woe, oh woe, he had neither. The symbol of his life was gone.

He rocked himself to and fro to the motion of the swaying lorry. Gone, gone. And gone too poor, pathetic little Symon Ravin with his head slashed off, and gone too, Paval Kaluta whom they'd tried to pull into shelter when the bullets were whipping across at ground level the day they had driven the Partisans to stand with their backs to the Dvina. And gone, despicably gone, Mikita Tomko the boon companion, the carefree and the brave, now a deserter skulking behind an uncle's shadow, or aunt's skirts. And now himself and his companions, after all their mighty efforts, after all their great sufferings, stripped and disgraced, and being driven ignominiously as vagabonds and suspects, to his own mother's birthplace to be doubted, and perhaps shot. It was more than flesh and blood could stand. Then he looked up and saw Ales Dubrovnii's red apple cheeks and brown, gentle country eyes, and there were two bright tears rolling down little Ales' cheeks, because he too was shamed and naked to the world. So then Sasha glanced away but wherever he looked he saw his own misery reflected, for even Kurt had his head on his arm and Josip Polyn's lips were twitching nervously. Only Michas, the mysterious one, with his calm and beautiful face, seemed secure because he smiled with a deep meaning at Sasha and his lips framed three words which Sasha couldn't hear but which he knew could only mean one thing and which Michas was breathing into the air, under the cold, reptilian eye of the German military policemen:

"Never say die."

And as Sasha, his eyes lighting on the instant, was about to make his reply, the first bomb fell.

The sudden roar of the attacking Shturmoviks coincided with the explosion of the first bomb. It fell ahead of the ammunition lorry and between it and a water-tanker. The tanker and its crew of two went up in a clutter of cast-iron and flesh that fell on to the surrounding vehicles in a shower. Then the rest of the planes swept in. The police lorry came to a halt with a jolt that sent Sasha sprawling on the floor as the driver fell over his wheel with a shrapnel splinter through his heart. There were shouts on all sides and a high-pitched, terrifying screaming. The Shturmoviks returned in line-ahead machine-gunning, the bullets ricochetting off the road between the vehicles and buzzing like hornets.

For the time being the confusion was complete, and it seemed clear to Sasha, finding himself shaken but unhurt as he picked himself up from the floor, that the attack must have come completely by surprise since it was only now that the armoured vehicles, far away at the head of the column, were opening fire. It could only mean a repetition of the same familiar story — the Russians were advancing more rapidly than had been thought possible.

No one in the police lorry had been touched, but the road was blocked before and behind, in one case by a newly made crater and in the other by a wrecked van. The two military policemen were down in the road doing what they could to restore order, and the "gruppe" of infantrymen in the next truck under an Oberfeldwebel was already occupied in tearing down the hedge to make gaps through which the column could be diverted. As Sasha reached out a hand to help Ales to his feet, the taller of the two guards shouted up from below with the order to get out of the lorry. A tyre had burst when the attack was at its height and it was necessary to change a wheel. The five prisoners dismounted and the guards led the little party into an adjacent field where the lorry followed. For one moment the thought darted through Sasha's mind to make a dash for it but he caught Michas's eye and the latter shook his head vehemently.

It took over three quarters of an hour to clear the road of debris. One by one the vehicles began to move into the adjoining meadow as they made the detour. It was growing very hot again and the dozen or more soldiers in the little truck had finished their vodka. Sasha and the others sat disconsolate in a corner of the meadow with their guard standing over them. Then suddenly from the corner of his eye Sasha saw the flash of the bottle in the air and instinctively ducked. The missile struck a stone and splintered.

They all heard the tinkle of the breaking glass and Sasha jumped to his feet as a second bottle followed and found its mark on his shoulder. Josip clapped a hand to his collarbone and swore. A guard yelled out an order to Kurt.

Kurt responded at once, immediately appreciating a situation which had caught all the others by surprise.

"Get back to the lorry," cried Kurt. "Quick... Quick!"

The lorry stood by the first gap that had been made, with its driver beside it wiping his hands on a lump of cotton waste. The new wheel was in place. Immediately behind him the smaller truck had disgorged its now half-intoxicated party. There were fourteen of them, private soldiers, without a non-commissioned officer in charge. They were arguing amongst themselves and shouting. A sergeant instructing the working party by the hedge called to them but they took no notice.

Kurt led the way to the lorry with one of the guards racing beside him. They alone seemed aware of what was happening. Sasha followed Kurt and arrived at the tail-board as a stone missed the other's head by inches. Then the complete party including the guards and the driver were clambering aboard.

"What the hell's all this about?" panted Sasha as Kurt pulled him down beside him in the shelter of the back-board. A guard was plucking at the press-button of his holster-flap feeling for the butt of the weapon.

"Somebody doesn't like us," said Kurt grimly. "And this is their way of showing it."

Another volley of stones struck the tail-board which had been hastily flung into place.

The guard with his Luger which he had now drawn, was yelling out to the working party at the gap. A sergeant with several men began to run towards the truck. Two more stones clattered on to the floor boards.

"The bastards," said Kurt. "I knew this would happen. They've been talking about us for the last half-hour. They're drunk and out of hand and think we're Russian prisoners."

It was all over in a few minutes. The arrival of the sergeant followed by an officer brought the incident to a close. The demonstrators were beaten off with the use of fists and a display of rifle butts. They staggered back to their own lorry as the line of vehicles began once more to move slowly forward. There were oaths and threats and laughter. The laughter predominated. Twenty minutes later the episode was forgotten.

Except for those concerned, it had been an amusing interlude, one of those occasions when feelings run high but when a dangerous situation can be averted by presence of mind. The guard who had given the order to Kurt in the first instance appeared to be aware of that fact. Not an inordinately vain man, nevertheless he felt justified in enlarging upon his perspicacity to his comrade. When he was done, Kurt for the benefit of his companions translated.

"Our friend here," said Kurt with considerable bitterness, "considers himself a clever fellow who has saved our skins for us. He has just told his mate that if he hadn't ordered us back to our lorry the moment he saw trouble brewing we could have been caught napping, and been badly beaten up, if not killed. Moreover, so he says if it hadn't been for him yelling all the time that we had not as yet been identified as Partisans, that we'd have been finished off. It seems to me," added Kurt with unusual acumen, "that the operative phrase is, 'as yet.'"

And with that Kurt closed his eyes, folded his arms, and with his back braced against the tail-board composed himself to sleep.

But the point he had made was true. Kurt for all his churlish ways could sometimes score a bull's eye. It was deadly true. There was a long way as yet to go before any of them could persuade himself that he was out of danger. Not indeed till they encountered one or more of their own people who could stand sponsor for them would that peril pass. Meanwhile the journey to Stalavichi must be completed. It seemed to Sasha, at the rate they were progressing that it could last for eternity.

Their position in the convoy since the Shturmoviks' attack had altered. They had moved a little farther ahead, out of range of their former assailants who were now prostrate in their own truck, under the supervision of an Oberfeldwebel. When they arrived at their destination they would awake from their drunken stupor to be charged with looting, insubordination, rioting, drunkenness and reprehensible conduct. But now they slept blissfully on, sublimely unaware of the wrath awaiting them, though as front-line troops they would not have allowed a little matter like that to have concerned them unduly. What harm, they would have argued, was there in beating up five bandits?

Nevertheless to Sasha, with his bitter, brooding thoughts, the situation appeared even more intolerable than it had before. Then the cruel doubts had seemed no more than injustice, but now he had experienced what the outcome of such doubts might mean in fact.

They were outcasts and every man's hand was against them. Moreover, they looked the part; dirty, ragged, unshaven and disreputable. With the change of position in the convoy he found that they were constantly ranging between two large trucks containing German soldiers. From their greater height the latter could look down into the smaller police car. Sometimes one of their party would exchange the time of day or a coarse pleasantry with the two guards. Then there would be laughter, and winks and gestures.

Sasha felt they were all directed against him and his companions. With no knowledge of German, and certainly none of its idiom, he could not distinguish between a jibe and mere curiosity. He burnt inwardly with shame and rage. If this long and wearisome retreat had been a rout, there would have been others in circumstances just as deplorable as themselves; other unfortunates without caps and badges and tunics and identification papers. But this was by no means a rout. Here was no stricken, vanquished army on the run. Admittedly from time to time they were being harassed, but the seemingly invincible German Wehrmacht was not as yet beaten, nor even thought that it might be. This, to their way of thinking, was still a strategic retreat according to plan. It was being carried out in a disciplined and orderly fashion. There might be unfortunate incidents inherent in such actions, but on the whole morale was high. No rumours of disaffection had yet filtered down to the rank and file.

It was five o'clock in the evening when the police lorry found a side road leading off to Stalavichi and, turning out of the convoy, accelerated and sped down the lane with an exhilarating burst of speed.

Nevertheless, to Sasha, stiff and sore and sick at heart at the thought of what still might come, it seemed a despicable home-coming....

13

So this, Sasha supposed, was the camp at Biallystok of which the Ukrainian sergeant had spoken...

It was ten-thirty of the fifth morning since they had left Stalavichi and had been interrogated by the Intelligence officer. That Biallystok could possibly prove their journey's end was beyond all hoping. That would have been far too good to be true. They could see the innumerable rows of wooden hutments and recognize them for what they were even before their new-found friend, the young Ukrainian sergeant whom they had picked up in the town, told them that they'd arrived at their destination. Every dawn of the last five days had found them with hopes raised high, every dusk with the self-same hopes dashed down. Five dawns and four dusks had taken their tally. Now another day was at hand, and their goal seemed still as far away as ever.

The Intelligence officer at Stalavichi five days ago had not in the first instance been at all favourably impressed. There was no question of any misunderstanding because he spoke their tongue perfectly so on that score everybody was at ease. On other scores they were definitely very ill at ease. It was the same inevitable problem of identification. After an hour of intense interrogation the execution stake seemed to Sasha nearer than ever; he could almost feel the pinioning rope around his arms. At the end of seventy minutes the Intelligence officer had flung down his pen in disgust.

"Take them away," he said. "And bring them up tomorrow. The situation may have cleared itself by then — if we're still here."

It was as they were being led across the school-playground whose adjacent buildings had been taken over as temporary headquarters that Ales saw his two countrymen. They were passing the wooden double-gates which had been left ajar. Ales began to shout in Ukrainian:

"Shuderich... Stepan Shuderich, come here. Symon Veter come to our help …"

He would have broken from the party had not one of the guards clapped a hand on his shoulder and spun him round, but Ales was still shouting and the two passing along the road outside halted in their tracks and then seeing who it was came running in. Both men were members of the battalion but of another company. Both were armed.

"Why it's Ales Dubrovnii. Why are you here? Who are these with you? Are you prisoners, there? Why are you prisoners? How did you escape those devils of Cossacks?"

Regardless of the guards they plied their questions and Ales gave the answers and then asked questions of his own. Oh! yes they had been very fortunate. Their own company had suffered a similar fate but not from a semi-organized massacre but from a mass-execution. Like No. 1 Company they had been marched to a rendezvous where others were already being stripped of their uniforms. One "gruppe" realizing the fate that awaited them and driven by desperation, had attempted to break away. The machine-guns had immediately been turned on them but Ales' two friends, during the sudden diversion, had contrived their escape.

"You will come with me to the Intelligence officer whom we have just left!" said Ales. "You can prove we are speaking the truth when we say we are allies of Germany... you will help your comrades…"

237

The Intelligence officer was crossing the playground when the guards accosted him and told him that one of the prisoners begged to speak with him. The Intelligence officer was far from pleased. He had had a long and tiring day interviewing and interrogating a vast number of persons of all kinds, classes, and ranks. He had never realized that there were so many satellite nations contributing to the cause of the Fatherland. He had seen with his experienced eye Rumanians, Latvians, Lithuanians, Ukrainians, Byelorussians and Estonians. Some had been in fair condition, and others, after a fortnight on the run, in very poor shape indeed; some had been satisfactorily disposed of, but many others who had not completed their identification either by document or insignia had been put back for further questioning as suspected spies or worse still, Partisans. The Intelligence officer had had quite enough of sorting people out for one day and wanted to get some supper, and see if his servant had managed to find some drinkable liquor. Nevertheless he listened to Ales and then to his two friends and at the end of it he said to the guards:

"I'll pass them on to Slonim. They can sort them out there, I've had enough of it. There's a truck due to leave for Slonim in half-an-hour's time with some Russian prisoners-of-war and three doubtful cases. Give them some food and get them on their way."

They had arrived at Slonim before midnight and slept in the open truck. All the journey the talk amongst themselves had been of the likelihood of the survivors of the battalion being temporarily quartered in the town. Their hopes had risen high because after so much endured the end could surely not be far off. But any views of what that end might be each one kept to himself. There was plenty of room in the truck because the guards had accompanied the Russian prisoners and the other suspects to their pen, and hadn't seemed to care much about them, but it was bitterly cold towards morning, and there had been no blankets.

At seven o'clock they had been given an indifferent breakfast of black bread and ersatz coffee. The guards had wholemeal bread and sausage and were allowed a whole billycan of coffee. At half-past eight the five of them went before a Wehrmacht officer, who scanned the report which the guard brought with them. He was a big, heavy-jowled man whose skin sagged under his chin and Sasha noticed he was unshaven. His eyes were red-rimmed with overwork and strain and there was a dried speck of white saliva at each corner of his mouth. He read the paper twice, turned it over, glanced at the back and then dropped it disdainfully into a battered wicker-work tray.

"All right," he said. "We'll accept your story. But my reports all tell me though that the survivors of your division have already gone through this God-forsaken hole and are re-grouping at Volkovysk which is another thirty miles or so on. Maybe you'll pick them up there, maybe you won't. You'd better take this chit to say you've been interrogated to my satisfaction." He scribbled on a sheet of paper, stamped it; signed it, and passed it to Ales.

They left the office disappointed that the battalion had left, but elated at the thought that it had passed through the town which meant they themselves were on the right track and that it wouldn't be long now till they were in the fold again. The threat of an untimely end had been temporarily removed.

It had been a good day's march to Volkovysk and they had made the passage on foot while the Wehrmacht transport groaned and grumbled past throughout the twenty four hours. No one had molested nor troubled to question them, because the retreat was still in full-swing, and not so far behind the Russian hordes were pressing on.

They had camped the first night out from Slonim in a meadow on the outskirts of Volkovysk and had made a nest for themselves in the long grass and clear of the footpath, but even so they were not to pass the night in peace.

An hour after midnight a German sergeant had literally stumbled upon them. They were lying huddled together for warmth — since the cold creeps in with the hunger — and the German, being in his cups and none too steady on his feet, had turned off the path and fallen over Josip who had been sleeping a little apart from the others. Josip had let out a yell and started to scramble to his feet while the sergeant had fallen heavily to the ground. But the latter was on his legs again by the time Josip was erect and without more ado both were locked in each other's arms in a desperate struggle.

The others were instantly awake, but momentarily bewildered by the sudden interruption of his sleep Sasha could only see two figures struggling frantically together in the moonlight. He sprang forward as soon as he could distinguish the one from the other, and attempted to take a hold of Josip's assailant by anything that would afford a grip, but his fingers had fumbled, and the sergeant had struggled free and the next minute had broken away from Josip as well.

He had backed away, groping desperately for his automatic, and cursing so that Kurt shouted to him that they were friends and allies and that if he would only keep his head, and hold his hand for a moment, the fact could be proved. Ales meanwhile was searching frenziedly for the chit he had received at Slonim. By the time he had found it all five of them were being threatened by the German's Luger. It had taken fully ten minutes after that, to convince him, drunk and distrustful as he was, that they were not the Partisans for which he had mistaken them.

On the following day as soon as it was daylight they had entered the town boldly and made enquiries of the soldiers they had seen in the streets, of any news of the division. But nobody seemed to know anything and a great many people whom they questioned were clearly suspicious, despite Ales' readiness to display his precious chit. By ten o'clock in the morning they were both hungry and disillusioned, but they made their way to the station and urged by Sasha in a sudden stroke of inspiration, Kurt made contact with the transport officer and asked his advice.

The transport officer who had disliked being accosted on his own platform by five ragamuffins, had told the Oberfeldwebel who accompanied him to attend to the enquiry, and the Oberfeldwebel had clicked his heels and saluted and then led Sasha's party to a bench in a crowded office where he left them and rejoined his officer. An hour and a half later he had returned having forgotten all about them. Nevertheless after his memory had been prompted the Oberfeldwebel scratching his ear, did seem to remember some troops answering that description passing through.

"Biallystok," he said. "Now I come to think of it... Biallystok. I remember who you're referring to. A very mixed crowd. What I would call a Foreign Legion." He had seemed to think that a pretty good joke, adding to Sasha, "And I'll warrant you never set foot in the Fatherland. Well, it's Biallystok, you should make for."

It had proved an eventful journey. They had caught the wrong train in the first instance and had been turned out at the last moment. The train was bound for Brest-Litovsk, but the Russians, they were told, were already in possession of the town. They jumped from the running-board and raced down the track and managed to climb aboard the right train as it was beginning to steam out of the station. It was crowded with German troops, and for some quite extraordinary reason, there were some Italians amongst them. But nobody had seemed concerned with the trend of events, and everybody had seemed friendly. Several of the Germans had shared their rations with Sasha's party when Kurt had told them their story, though he was careful to stress the brutality of the Tartars and Cossacks, and not the shortcomings of any Wehrmacht officer.

They drew near Biallystok a couple of hours after dusk but came to a stop six miles from the town. It was under bombardment by the Red Air Force with the Luftwaffe night-fighters attempting to intercept. Not till dawn came did they dare to approach nearer; they spent the night in the train. But with first light they drew at last into the station.

The town was still burning and a canopy of black smoke hung motionless above it. There had been very few civilians in the streets but a considerable number of troops assembling for entraining to the west. Over everything was an atmosphere of uneasy restlessness and urgency, but there was still no panic.

At eight o'clock as the first drops of rain began to fall from a grey sky, Kurt seized the opportunity of accosting a Wehrmacht officer as he stopped in the street to lace a boot.

He had been an affable young man, over-anxious to impress with his eagerness to be of assistance to any lame dog. Did he know, Kurt enquired, anything at all of the Field Police Division, reported to be reforming somewhere in this district?

Certainly he knew. He couldn't say he was part and parcel of the outfit nor that he had any connexions with it, because after all they were all good fellows of course, but not quite the real thing which wasn't the same thing, was it? Nevertheless no one, he rattled on, especially these days, could afford to neglect any assistance when it was offered, therefore it was quite understandable that legionnaires could be very acceptable.

"Legionnaires!" Kurt exclaimed. "Is it a legionary unit which you are talking about, Herr Lieutenant? Because that is what we are looking for."

"You must make for Grodno," said the young Lieutenant. "Definitely Grodno. It's about thirty miles farther on to the north. I expect the trains are still running. Nevertheless one can always walk, can't one?"

"One can," said Kurt, resignedly, remembering the miles they had left behind.

"You'll find them all there," said the Lieutenant. "There are Latvians and Ukrainians and White Russians, the whole bag of mixed biscuits! They are reforming under German officers and then there will be a great rear-guard action to cover the retreat of our armies until we turn to make our stand. It has all been thought out and is very sound. Well, that is where you should find your people. *Auf wiedersehen.*"

He had flashed them a cheerful smile and, turning up his collar against the rain, left them. Half an hour later on the road to Grodno they had met the young Ukrainian sergeant. He had been coming down the road in the opposite direction, and they had stopped him to make certain that they were going the right way. He was wearing the uniform of the Field Police and his face seemed vaguely familiar to Sasha. He carried a rifle and complete equipment.

Sasha had asked if they were right for Grodno and the sergeant said that they certainly were, and then little Ales had confided that they were looking for their own people and naming them, asked if the sergeant had ever heard of them.

243

"I have," the sergeant had said. "Because I'm one of them myself. And I think I recognize you. You were in No. 1 Company, if I remember. I was in charge of No. 1 Platoon of No. 3 with Lieutenant Wald who was one of the first to get on his horse that happy Sunday morning. Why do you want to go to Grodno? Our people are here."

"Here!" said Sasha. "We were told by a German officer —"

"You don't want to listen to German officers," said the Ukrainian sergeant. "Half of them don't know what they are talking about, but the trouble is they won't admit it. It wouldn't fit in with their estimation of themselves, so what they don't know they invent. What else did he tell you? That they were going to fight a rear-guard action that would make the retreat from Moscow look like a picnic?"

"Something like it," said Sasha.

"They'll do the fighting when the time comes," said the other, "but we'll have paved the way for it over our dead bodies. I can see what the idea is. The German armies will pull out while we screen their backsides. Now this is the way you want to go. If you'll turn back with me I'll put you on the right road. There's a camp near a causeway which was a Wehrmacht Training Depot and which your people are using for the time being. I can't take you all the way because I've a train to catch — if there is one — down to Belsen for special duties and God knows what that means. I'd rather be going in the opposite direction. Come along then."

They had turned back down the road to Biallystok with the rain in their faces, but joy in their hearts. The sergeant had left them at a cross-roads with the injunction to take the first lane to the right which after a quarter of a mile would lead to a causeway. This they should cross and they would find that it would lead to the old Training Depot Camp. They couldn't mistake it, nor lose the way. Then they had bidden the sergeant goodbye and good luck, and thanking him for the hundredth time, had set out with the conviction that their objective was reached at last. It had been, then, something after nine o'clock of the fifth day after they had left Stalavichi. It was now approaching half-past ten of the same day.

This was the camp. There was no mistaking it. The roofs of the rows and rows of dreary wooden huts, glistened in the rain. The first gentle fall had developed into something that at times approached a deluge. Sasha supposed there was a thunderstorm about. He couldn't have cared if there were twenty thunderstorms and each one worse than the last.

This was the camp all right. There was the causeway and here were the huts and the wire-fencing, the derelict guardroom and the striped pole across the barrier gate. There was a pile of saturated waste-paper by a swill tub and a couple of buckets, one with the bottom out and the other with a broken handle, perched on what might once have been the orderly-room steps. The rain splashed down from a choked gutter and a rag flapped dismally from a strand of barbed wire.

They sat in a row, disillusioned and despairing, on a rickety bench beneath a rusty sheet of corrugated iron on four wooden uprights. All five were drenched through and cluttered with mud to the ankles. In the distance a motionless cloud, darker than the rain clouds above them, told them that Biallystok still burned. Even from here they could smell the sour tang of wet and yet smouldering timber. Soon the Russian armour would be following up the bombardment. Sasha seemed to remember that it was usually described as a "softening-up process." He supposed that it might be equally applied to masses of metal as well as masses of flesh and muscle.

The five of them sat silent on the bench beneath the sheet of corrugated iron, and the rain beat down and ran in dribbling small streams from the rusty edge of their inadequate shelter. No one spoke, because each was too sick at heart. Did anyone anywhere know anything about anything? If a German officer, with possibly all the best intentions in the world, directed them to Grodno, then an Ukrainian sergeant told them that Biallystok was the place and that the German was a liar. So it had been ever since they had made contact with the Wehrmacht; from Volna to Stalavichi, on to Slonim and Voikovysk, and at last here, at Biallystok. And at Biallystok the town was on fire and the long-sought camp was empty — for no place had ever looked so deserted. And again Sasha told himself they were nobody's responsibility and no one cared. They had fought gallantly, escaped a dreadful slaughter, and now their only use was to act as a screen, to clutter up the roads in the face of the advancing enemy.

Somebody was coming down between the huts. They could hear him whistling through the rain. Sasha thought to himself: "Good God, there's another living soul in this God-forsaken place. What the hell's he looking for?" The sound of footsteps drew nearer and the squelch of rubber-boots in mud. He began to rise wearily from the bench and face about. If only from force of habit he might as well ask the way. Unless of course it was a bloody Cossack. Could the Cossacks have got as far as this already? He was damned if he cared. The owner of the rubber-boots came round a hut and stopped face to face with Sasha.

Next to Nicola's he would have known those eyes anywhere in the world. They were bright and shining and it seemed there were little flecks of gold in them. The white teeth were gleaming behind lips parted in a twisted, half-humorous, smile.

"Why, it's the little 'kutscher'." said Sergeant Karol. His arm was in a sling. "We're all down the other end of the camp. The huts don't leak there. We've got Major Shaeffer with us. Tomorrow we move to Lomza to reform. How are you 'kutscher'?"

14

Three weeks later Major Shaeffer, now promoted Colonel by Herr Himmler, Chief of the State Police, held a parade at Lomza and made a brief speech. All those present on parade, which consisted of all the legionnaires of all units who had escaped the Russians, were in uniform and re-equipped with rifles. The survivors of the 34th Battalion numbering altogether twenty-two men out of an original total of six hundred, were paraded on the right of the line. Sasha with his five comrades in the rank stood to attention.

Oberst Shaeffer in his speech told the officers and men assembled before him that he was now in command of the battalion which would shortly move on to a training camp in East Prussia, where the re-grouping and re-forming and re-arming would be completed, and the battalion would then go into intensive training for special duties which had been allotted to them by the Chief of Police. The establishment and organization of the battalion would be as it had always been, an officer of the Legionnaires doubled with an officer of the Wehrmacht and so on. In future the battalion would form one of the units of the famous division known as the Storm Grenadiers. This honour had been granted in recognition of the loyalty of all those, including the survivors of the massacre of 2 July, 1944, who had in the hour of temptation, refrained from deserting or going over to the Partisans, thus remaining loyal to their German allies.

Colonel Shaeffer, his speech concluded, walked with his Adjutant and Headquarters' Officers to the right of the line, where he halted, facing the twenty-two survivors of 2 July, and saluted. He then passed along the rank and shook each man by the hand.

A month later in Ciechanow where the division was stationed for training, little Ales, who with his guileless ways could extract secrets from any ordinary sphinx, asked Sergeant Karol where he thought they would eventually be posted. The latter, who thought Ales was a tough little nut, and dead crafty under his innocent manner, and knowing that it was an open secret anyway, replied:

"You might as well get killed on the Western Front in France as anywhere else, mightn't you?"

All of which Ales repeated to Sasha, Kurt, Michas and Josip since for the time being they were still in their original "gruppe." Sasha said:

"He's a saucy one, is old Karol. What *I* say is: 'Never say die.'" It was the first time that any one of them had used the phrase since Mikita had thrown his hand in.

The last weeks of August, 1944, were approaching together with Sasha's seventeenth birthday.

PART THREE: A MUTINY AND AFTER

1

There was a rumour afoot, a very sinister rumour. Sasha thought that the little group in the corner of the barrack room were discussing it now by the way the headquarters' orderly, and the dispatch rider, Hans and Karl cast furtive glances over their shoulders every time the unoiled hinges of the door creaked. He hated the sound, because being intermittent it kept him awake for most of the night, so that he wished they could be back sleeping in the open under their "plandeckes." Moreover since the R.A.F. had intensified their attacks on Vesoul, and they themselves had been moved into the barracks, there seemed to be every chance of being buried alive.

They had left Ciechanow after Lomza, travelling across Germany during the last days of August, and reaching Vesoul in Western France in the first week of September. At Ciechanow the division had reorganized and reformed, drilling, parading and taking part in field exercises, being armed with rifles and light machine-guns and automatic weapons. They had no anti-tank guns and no heavy artillery. In persuading the Reichsfuhrer of the Police to regroup the survivors of the original Field Police Division and use them on the Western Front against the Maquis, Colonel Shaeffer had doubtless saved, for the time being at any rate, hundreds of his men's lives. Had they been disbanded and returned to their families whose territory was now being over-run by the victorious advancing Russians, scarcely one out of ten would have survived their vengeance. On the Western Front the Americans with the French 1st Army under Marshal de Lattre de Tassigny had swept across France all the way from the Côte d'Azur on the Mediterranean and were now embattled before Belfort in the Vosges in the north-east of France and might soon be on the very banks of the Rhine.

It was difficult for Sasha to say when the spirit of disillusionment and discontent had first become apparent. Looking back to the days in the packed troop-train that had carried them across Germany to France, he could suppose that the undeniable evidence of the Allied bombing seen every day and heard each night, had started everyone thinking. At times the damage appeared so completely devastating that it seemed inconceivable that any semblance of order might ever be restored.

Moreover, the division's incentive to fight seemed to be on the decline. Sasha and his friends had discussed it, albeit with caution and in subdued tones amongst themselves, for Kurt and little Ales were still their daily companions, though Michas and Josip had been posted to a newly reformed battalion when at Lomza, and Sergeant Karol was in command of another platoon in No. 3 Company.

Even Kurt, once a good Party man who would brook no criticism, had modified his views. No one could forget for one moment and for all the rest of his natural life, the disgraceful spectacle of the Wehrmacht officers galloping at full tilt, away from the advancing enemy and away from their own deserted men, on a certain sunlit Sunday morning some two months previously.

That, indeed, was one point though it was never pressed home out of deference to Kurt's feelings. But there was another and it arose from homesickness.

In the first days at Vesoul before the battalion had moved into barracks they had slept in the open fields under their "plandeckes." The barracks had not been prepared for them as they had in the other towns where the rest of the division was billeted. The three of them shared one tent, and in the lull of one midnight-bombing little Ales had growled:

"I wish I were home."

"Home," said Sasha. "That's a good many miles away."

And his thoughts had turned to Radzimichy, and quite suddenly he seemed to be seated on a corn-bin in the stables and the pony was munching at his midday feed, snuffling his nose into chaff and every now and again raising a hind-leg in a half-kick of ecstasy, and stamping a hoof on the stone flags. The sun was streaming through the open door, and through Valia's golden hair as she leant against the door-post, and outside the chickens were clucking and the old sow grunting. He had felt suddenly desolate and lonely.

Then there had been a fierce glow in the sky seen through the tent slit, and the earth had begun to tremble again as a second wave of the enemy bombers had arrived.

"Yes, home," said Ales, not to be interrupted by any bombardments once he was committed to a theme. "I keep on thinking of it. I don't believe we shall ever see our homes again."

"If you can't keep cheerful," said Kurt. "Keep your mouth shut."

"It was worth while doing our best then," said Ales, "Because we were fighting for something."

"Well, aren't we now?" said Kurt. "You had better hold your tongue or you'll be getting into trouble."

"We may be called the Storm Grenadiers now," said Ales. "But we had something to fight for then — our own independence."

"Germany will still reward her allies when she's won the war," said Kurt, "And you will have your own independence."

"We were fighting the Communists in Russia," said Sasha. "That is what I liked to think. They are my enemy, not because they were Partisans but because they were Communists. Will it be the same fighting these Maquis, these Frenchmen who are just patriots? I don't think I have the same heart to kill."

There the argument had ended but it was typical of its kind which was daily increasing, filtering down from the higher levels of the non-commissioned ranks. Now in the barrack room Sasha was certain the refrain had been taken up again, and he made a significant gesture to Ales who occupied a bed next to him. Kurt slept in one opposite. They were rough-and-ready affairs, being composed of straw palliasses with a couple of blankets, and quite half of them were merely three planks on low wooden trestles, but after the open fields the change should have been welcome. That it was not was due to the ferocity of the British bombing. Only the night before last, Vesoul station had been practically demolished; and the station was scarcely a quarter of a mile away.

Karl, who was prominent amid the group in the corner and had been carried away a little with the news which he was burning to impart, raised his voice.

"I was told the same story in Luva and then again in Luxeuil, riding through today with dispatches for headquarters. Ten of them in Luva and another four in Luxeiul ... seven officers and seven sergeants, and all the officers were from the staff college at Minsk ..." The speaker dropped his voice, glanced round about him, and continued in an inaudible, agitated whisper that would not carry across the room, but a moment later his last words, before the door was flung open, could be plainly heard... "It is nothing short of mutiny!" Then the rest died on the dispatch-rider's lips as the orderly sergeant stood planted in the doorway, his hands on his hips, and his head inclined a little to one side as of a man hard of hearing intent on catching a key-word.

"It's past time for Lights Out." said the Orderly Sergeant. "Have I got to tell you every night?"

It was fully twenty minutes to go and everybody knew it, but no one raised a murmur. Very soon the R.A.F. would be over again, so what the hell was the sense of fixing a time for Lights Out when very shortly they would have no more rest. Moreover, the phrase was pointless since there was precious little light to begin with, only a flickering flame from an old paraffin storm-lantern which someone had found and hung on the wall. They all knew that the sergeant had been ordered to put forward the hour of his rounds so that he might, inadvertently as it were, overhear any tittle-tattle.

An hour later when Sasha had fallen into his first, deep sleep the sudden crash of the falling "stick" sent him rolling out of his blankets and under the bed. By the luck of the draw, he was the proud possessor of a wrought iron bedstead of which there were only a dozen in the whole company.

He lay under his bed, his blankets clutched around him and his steel helmet perched on his cheek-bone, covering the upper side of his face and head. The protection of both bed and helmet were so hopelessly inadequate that in the morning he would grin ruefully at the recollection of the previous night, but at the time the frail iron-frame-work above him restored his confidence. In time the crash of detonating bombs ceased and the plaster stopped falling from the ceiling so that he crawled out from his improvised shelter and pulled the blankets round him on his bed. There he lay like a log till reveille.

They had begun specialized training the day they had arrived in Vesoul and the other three battalions at Luva and Luxeuil had followed suit. Each day at Vesoul a routine order was posted up giving the following day's detail of duty. As he thrust the bed clothes aside the following morning, Sasha remembered that today his own company was due for a Field exercise, while at least one of the others would be occupied on the barrack square and the machine-gun company would be down at the range. It was a bright sunlit morning in the third week of September.

He washed, dressed, and went down the stone stairs to the mess-room with Kurt and Ales. They ate their breakfasts, returned to their barrack room, checked their ammunition and equipment, and prepared for first parade at eight o'clock. At the stroke of the hour they fell in under their corporal and the roll-call was taken. The battalion officers of the Wehrmacht numbered twenty, including Lieutenant Schwabe, who with his legionnaire opposite number, young Sergeant Shuderich from the Ukraine, was now in command of No. 1 Platoon. By half-past eight the battalion commander had come on parade and all officers had taken post. The Germans were outnumbered by the legionnaires in the ratio of fifty to one.

At twenty minutes to nine the heavy machine-gun company moved off from the square. They departed in the usual order but instead of making for the transport section to pick up their horse-drawn limbers, they were given the command to "right turn" where the road which ran alongside the parade ground led to the armoury. The other three infantry companies were stood at ease. Sasha in the rear rank of No. 1 Platoon, began to wonder if any alteration had been made in the day's programme. They should have been marching out of the barrack gates by now for their rendezvous with an Engineer platoon for their field exercise. Then he noticed that No. 1 Company had been brought to attention and that the German commanders were moving slowly along the ranks of their platoons. Ten minutes later with No. 1 Company called to order, Lieutenant Schwabe with the assistance of a corporal and two men carrying buckets stood before Sasha. The buckets were half-full of unused small arms ammunition.

"Hand over your ammunition," said the lieutenant. He was a small, sandy-haired young man with thick lensed glasses in steel frames. He stood blinking his eyes and moistening his Ups with the tip of his tongue as Sasha opened his pouches and drew out the clips of cartridges. A corporal held the bucket out and Sasha dropped in the live rounds. He wondered idly what might be the object in collecting ammunition when they were due to depart for a day in the field. It was not like the Germans at any time to disarm their men when occupying enemy territory. Still it was none of his business. Then it was Ales' turn who was next to him and he too was emptying his pouches. Kurt, in the front rank, had already made his contribution.

It was not till a quarter to ten that No. 1 Company was given the order to move. They left the square, passed through the barrack gates, and into the town. The streets were deserted except for the gangs of air raid rescue parties and workmen busy with pick and shovel at the foot of demolished buildings and by the great heaps of rubble. The company moved in platoons in the single file artillery order. Sasha thought it was a pity they couldn't have marched in column and kept proper step. It would have brightened things up. Somehow there was something very wrong with this bright, autumn day. There was a feeling of uneasiness in the air. He couldn't get out of his mind's eye the spectacle of little Lieutenant Schwabe licking his lips as if he were nervous. He was at the head of the platoon now and when they rounded a corner Sasha could see him stumping along in his big boots. Now and again he would look over his shoulder as if he suspected something or wondered if his men were still following him. Then he would shout an order to keep proper distance and close up. He seemed on edge and Sasha thought that even old Kubik had been preferable to a little, scruffy man with sandy hair and freckles.

At the first halt he sat down by the hedge with Ales. They had reached more open country by now but there was still no sign of the engineer platoon which they were supposed to meet. He remarked on the point to Ales.

"They've got themselves lost," said Ales.

"They can go on getting lost for all I care," said Sasha.

Ales, in his queer, astute way, glanced up at this old soldier whom he admired.

"What's come over you?" he said. "You'd have bitten your tongue off for talking like that, when I first met you."

"Nothing's come over me," said Sasha, annoyed with himself, and then immediately repenting, "What's the matter with today?"

"I don't know," said Ales. "But I feel the same way."

A minute or two before the whistle went Kurt left the company of Hans with whom he had been talking, crossed the road, and joined them. There was a frown on his forehead and that portentous expression on his face that Ales called "Kurt's Commander-in-Chief look". It generally heralded a heavy half-hour of Stalingrad reminiscences.

"Well," said Sasha. "Have you taken all the troubles of the world upon your shoulders? You look as if you had."

"I've been talking with that headquarters orderly," said Kurt. "He's been telling me that the dispatch rider was passing through Luxeuil and Luva yesterday and he heard the same story in both places, from separate sources."

"And what might that story be?", said Ales, with a grin.

"It is very bad," said Kurt. "I know what my old colonel would have thought about it all."

"Oh! damn your old colonel," said Sasha indulgently. "Come to the point."

"Don't you speak disrespectfully of a fine officer," said Kurt. "You don't find that kind among this mob."

"So I've noticed," said Sasha.

"Well, I'll tell you what I'm talking about," said Kurt, always ready to be goaded into justifying himself. "It's *mutiny*."

There was a long pause. Ales perched in the hedge, his rifle propped up besides him, stared up at Kurt with his solemn face, till the latter shook his head like a troubled old man, which to Sasha's way of thinking made him look ludicrous; and because the little red mischievous imps of a suspicious morning were prompting him, Sasha burst out into a guffaw of laughter, more scornful than he intended.

Kurt flushed to his forehead.

"*Mutiny*," he repeated. "Fourteen in all, officers and sergeants, mostly Ukrainians and Byelorussians. They'll all be shot of course. They're under close arrest now."

"Of course they mutiny," said Sasha, grinning away like the little ape that he looked at the moment, determined to forestall any attempt on Kurt's part to enjoy his precious morsel of scandal, however serious this might be.

"Of course they mutiny," said Sasha again. "If it was only on account of the food, not to say anything of being posted a million miles from home in order to fight a people we've no quarrel with. Who wants to shoot the French and Tommies or the Americans? They've never done us any harm, that I know of."

"You are not a German," said Kurt, not without dignity. "And you are not one of us. You are a foreigner and the Wehrmacht wouldn't own you. So there is no disgrace to you in that ugly word 'mutiny'."

There were tears of anger in Kurt's eyes and Sasha knew that this needless, senseless, quarrel should stop, before it got out of hand; before both were hurt. And he knew that it was going that way because this sinister morning had somehow taken hold of them, and that here, in the bright September sunshine, the repressed and pent-up emotions of months of strain were suddenly boiling over.

"You will never be an officer —" said Kurt.

"God forbid —" said Sasha.

"— and you will never lead your men into action as I shall. All my family were soldiers and gentlemen so you wouldn't know what mutiny means to a regiment, because your father and his father before him were moujiks and their sons were only 'kutschers'."

Sasha got up from his seat in the hedge and his fists were clenched.

"You can take that back, you bloody Nazi," he said, "Or I'll ram the words down your gullet."

From the far end of the long file of men a whistle shrilled and then another.

"Fall in," yelled Lieutenant Schwabe, completely oblivious to any dissensions within his ranks.

At half-past twelve of that midday No. 1 Company arrived back in the barracks at Vesoul. They formed into columns, quarter of a mile from the town, and marched in through the gates like soldiers. Once inside, the gates clanged together behind them and the company were halted and dressed. They were then ordered to "pile arms," and were dismissed in good time for their midday meal. There had been no rendezvous with any Engineer platoon nor attempts at any field exercise.

At one o'clock, when all personnel of the four companies of the battalion were still eating in their mess, the General Alarm suddenly sounded.

Everyone ran from the dining-room, clattering down the stone stairway, and cramming their caps on their heads, streaming out of the main doorway into the barrack square. The gongs, syrens, and rattles, were sounding together and the steam-hooter was blowing great gasps of panic. As the men jostled and pushed and crossed each other's tracks to find their markers, and their places in platoon and "gruppe," the German officers with their legionnaire counterparts came down the steps of the officers mess. Regardless of their individual commands they split into two groups as if intent on moving together as a body, and took up a position facing the men, as the adjutant with the commanding officer at his side gave the order which brought the battalion into line. No man of the rank and file was armed, because the weapons which had been piled on the square before the midday dismissal had in the dinner interval mysteriously disappeared.

The indescribable cacophony of the alarm ceased just as suddenly as it had begun. The hooter expired with one hollow groan and the syren wailed into silence. Eight hundred men, with looks of bewilderment on their puzzled features, stared from one to another wondering how they had reached their present position and why; and in many cases, so great had been the intended confusion, who their neighbour might be. Sasha, elbow to elbow with little Ales, could see no other familiar face and wondered to what "gruppe" he might unwittingly have attached himself.

Then raising his head and peering over the heads of the rank before him, he saw with an instant and appalling pang of fear, an object and then another of its kind that explained by its silent and sinister presence, what everything was all about.

Immediately opposite the disarmed battalion stood the main barrack block. A similar but smaller block stood on either flank. The brickwork in every instance was of a dirty, yellow-grey, colour and there were three rows of windows with blackened panes in each building. The upper portions of the windows of the top and bottom rows were open a few inches at the top to assure the essential and standard ventilation as laid down in orders. But in the middle row of windows the sashes had been thrown up and the bottom half was wide open. In every fourth open window of the middle row the ugly muzzle of a machine-gun, duly deflected to hold a portion of the doomed battalion in its sights, pointed defiantly downwards.

The blood ran cold in Sasha's veins, and there was a constriction round his throat as if a cold steel hand was closing on his wind-pipe. He could see the little black hole that was the gas condenser shield at the end of each gun's muzzle, and behind, within the immediate shadowing recesses of each room, the ghost-like faces of the gun-crew. He licked his lips because they were dry with the terrible fear within him. Then he glanced down and saw little Ales staring up wide-eyed at him and knew that he too had seen the menace that threatened them all. Like two figures of stone they stared hypnotized with the horror in each other's eyes, till each slowly turned again towards the barrack blocks and lifted his eyes to the row of open windows. As they did so, their companions on either side also looked up. At once the contagious fear swept down the ranks of the battalion.

There was a clatter, and now far out on the right flank of the line came the voices of the officers shouting orders. Some movement was taking place but it did not concern Sasha nor his platoon at all, for nobody stirred though the muffled voices continued. Sasha looked round for Kurt but couldn't see him, and told himself that he was lost in the initial scramble to get on parade and that, if they survived this fearful day, he would at the first opportunity approach him and apologize for his part in the morning's fatuous quarrel.

If they survived! For now several of the gun-muzzles in the blank windows were moving to and fro very slightly as the crews re-aligned their sights. And Sasha thought to himself that even the hideous afternoon of slaughter on a certain Sunday was preferable to this nightmare form of suspense, when no man knew at what moment the guns would spit forth bullets. So, because there was nothing else to do, he stood stock-still with his hands down by his sides, as Nicola had once stood, waiting to be shot down like a dog.

Then the German officers were at the head of No. 1 Company. Sasha could hear them shouting. Why did Germans always have to shout? Was it because they wanted to make out they were bigger and braver than everybody else, or did they do it when they wanted to conceal their own fear?

There were four of them coming down the ranks and immediately behind them were two legionnaire officers and two sergeants. As they came to each man they paused before him, passed some brief comment, and moved on. In most cases under the guidance of a sergeant the men fell out of their places in the company ranks and fell in again with a squad that was being formed on the right. It was immediately apparent to

Sasha what was happening; the sheep were being separated from the goats.

So this then could be the end to all his aspirations and hopes. They were seeding them out one by one regardless of their nationality, past character, creed or record. What this end would be he could only guess. They were "making an example" of them, because there was disaffection in the 30th S.S. Storm Grenadier Division, because there was mutiny in the air, and in fact, at Luva and Luxeuil. The innocent might well suffer with the guilty. What did that matter as long as an "example was made?" They were only the Field Police legionnaires.

Nor, on this shameful occasion, was there any opportunity to fight back. He and the others had made a dash for it on that unforgettable Sunday afternoon, and they had survived. Now they were held like sheep in the slaughterhouse.

Somebody was tapping his chest and a voice was bellowing in his ear to get a move on. They were turning him round, pushing him on his way, and Ales was behind him. He couldn't properly make out who they were because he was dazed and sick with it all and horribly frightened, but they were certainly new officers. His stomach was turning over inside him, and he was astonished that he could contain himself. He was trying to do what they demanded, and to move to where they wanted him to go and join the ranks of the damned, but his legs wouldn't move. Then he heard a voice say:

"Not these two, sir, they'll pass. I can vouch for them."

Then he was stepping back into the ranks again with Ales, and the little group of officers and sergeants was passing on down the long line of terrified men, and automatically he was shuffling along, closing in to the right because there were now great gaps in the ranks of No. 1 Company. But before the officers passed he looked for the moment into the cat-like eyes of Sergeant Karol.

That night he waited beside his bed in the dark for a long time without undressing. Ales, subdued and exhausted with the day's events, had crept into bed before lights out and was sleeping like a child. The orderly sergeant had made his rounds and this time he had been accompanied by the orderly officer. There had been a great deal of furtive whispering and conjecture amongst the ones that were left before they came, for there were many empty places where men had slept. There was one empty bed opposite Sasha.

The orderly officer, a big, blustering fellow, had stood with his legs straddled apart and his thumbs tucked into his belt, while his fingers played round the flap of his pistol holster.

"So these are the good boys," he said to the sergeant.

The sergeant had replied:

"Yes, Herr Lieutenant, these are the ones we decided *not* to give a free ticket for the Dachau express."

Then they had laughed heartily at what they considered a very funny joke. That was a couple of hours ago and Sasha was still unready for bed. Someone had taken over Kurt's bed, because he was not with them any longer. Sasha thought of Kurt waiting with the hundreds of others on the semi-demolished platform of Vesoul Station. Kurt hadn't been lucky and hadn't caught Sergeant Karol's eye. Kurt was going to Dachau and the gas-chamber with all the other naughty boys. Kurt, the good Party man and soldier, who had fought bravely before Stalingrad, would never be an officer now and lead his men into action and maybe die a good death of which his father and his grandfather, and all the rest of them, would have been proud. Kurt was going to die like a rat, gassed in its rat-hole, because somebody had got to take the blame and indeed, what, even if a mistake had been made, was another dead man amongst so many? But the pity was that now he'd never be able to tell Kurt that the quarrel in the morning had been a mistake which he now most deeply regretted. He wouldn't be able to apologize and say he was sorry; any more than he would ever be able to explain to Nicola that he hadn't betrayed his own home; any more than he'd ever be likely to see that home again in the sunlight with the pigs and chickens; even the pony might be dead and gone by now, and Papa gone funny in his head with all his strange thoughts, and his pepper-flavoured vodka; and Valia could have lost her beauty with her innocence, and Walter lying dead or dying.

He lay face downwards on his blankets and bit into the rough material to control himself. But one sob escaped like an enormous belch, so that out of the darkness a voice said:

"Who the hell's that? For God's sake stop that bloody row. I want to sleep."

2

The following morning the survivors of the mutiny of the 30th Division Byelorussian were re-issued with their arms and ammunition. The establishment of the division had been roughly halved with those shot, and those confined behind the wire at Dachau. Few escaped the gas-chamber. By the end of September after a week patrolling the railway bridge at Vesoul, Colonel Shaeffer's battalion received orders to proceed by stages to Schlettstadt, approximately sixty miles northwest of the great fortress of Belfort, and ten miles from the Rhine. Though there had been one or two brushes with the Maquis at Vesoul, who came down raiding from the hills, the intention, it was said, when the division had reassembled in Alsace, was to train them in anti-paratroop fighting. The technique would not be so far removed from that of contending with the Partisans.

Or was it that the division was in disgrace and wouldn't be trusted again except in extreme emergency, and this was as good an excuse as any to keep them out of the way? Moreover, what was the source of that strange rumour that the division would soon be on its way to Czechoslovakia to defend Prague? And anyway what was the sound reasoning for training a body of men as specialist troops when there were still frequent deserters in their midst including one Iron Cross man who had saved his officer's life? And when only two days off from Mussik in the forced march from distant Vesoul, a German sergeant was beaten to death by a Byelorussian "kutscher" who confessed and was shot, could anyone speak of the division with any assurance that there was complete unity within its ranks? And if their sole transport was still horses, and their night's shelter with the greatest of luck was a barn, or with the more usual fortune, the brief respite of a "plandecke," against the weather, and, if they were still lacking anti-tank weapons and any kind of artillery, who could describe them as front-line troops and fit to take the foremost place in battle?

And pressing relentlessly forward, sweeping all before them, still south of Belfort, the opposing French and American armies were driving on.

3

"If only it wasn't for the food." Hans, the headquarters orderly who had shared a barrack-room with Sasha when Kurt was alive, was always grumbling about it. He was a tall, overgrown, dismal youth with spectacles who had been brought up in a suburb of pre-war Berlin by a widowed aunt. His parents had both died tragically; his father after a beating-up by the Gestapo for some political misdemeanour, and his mother by her own hand when the news of her husband's death was brought to her.

Hans, a lucky survivor of the mutiny, had given up his work as an orderly room clerk and volunteered as a sharpshooter as soon as the battalion had gone into anti-paratroop training on their arrival at Mussik. Now he was with Sasha and Ales in a barn behind the dilapidated farmhouse where the survivors of No. 1 Company were billeted. They had been quartered in the village for the last six weeks and the conditions were daily growing worse. All ten men of the "gruppe" who slept in the barn, including Ianka Valoda, the number-one of Sasha's machine-gun to which he had been promoted, wore a week's growth of beard. When in the first week of November the battalion had been issued with "bazookas" the light-machine guns had been replaced by the heavier "thirty-fours." Ales was the ammunition carrier to Ianka's gun.

The ten men lay wrapped in their blankets on the bare stone floor of the barn. At the far end of the building where the rays of the single lantern could not penetrate, the horses stamped their hooves on the cobbles, and the air was heavy with the ammoniated odour of their sweat. But this evening the food had been reasonably palatable and there had been plenty of it. Two nights before the Tommies had come over with their bombers and hit their horse lines. To troops grown only too accustomed to one billycan of sour soup, horse-flesh was a delicacy.

Sasha lay with his ground-sheet over him because the roof leaked in unexpected places and it was impossible to find a dry spot. Ales squatted beside him and Ianka Valoda sat with his back to one of the timber supports to the quaking roof. He was a young Byelorussian who had served for some time with an anti-tank battalion and had come to No. 1 Company as an instructor on the "bazookas," and had now reverted to his original trade. He was as usual criticizing one of the German officers, Lieutenant Litzmann who, newly appointed, was in charge of the machine-gun company.

"He is a bag of wind. He tells everyone that his uncle was the great General Litzmann of the First World War, and was personally decorated by the Kaiser."

Somebody was hammering at the double-door which Sasha had bolted against the onslaughts of the gusty night. The rain that had leaked through the cracks between the rotting planks had formed a pool as black as ink.

"Open up! Open up!"

It was the voice of Sergeant Weber, who was on duty and he was thumping on the door with both fists. Ales unwrapped the blanket which he was holding round his shoulders and went to the door and pulled back the bolt. Sergeant Weber stood on the threshold with the rain running off the tip of his nose into his big moustache.

"Come on," he said. "We're on the move. Parade in the street in twenty minutes. Get a move on there. Get a move on."

The weeks of dull routine training on half rations were over. It was a quarter past nine of the night of 16 November and the Lorraine offensive had opened and the battle for Metz begun. Every man was needed by the German High Command, whatever his rating as a trained fighting man, however ill-equipped for the purpose.

They were out on parade in twenty-five minutes which was very good time considering the weather. The rain came down in a steady downpour. Within the next half-hour No. 1 Company had got aboard the single-decker buses which had miraculously appeared out of the darkness and the first two platoons of No. 2 Company were hard on their tails. In the dining-room of a requisitioned mansion Oberst Shaeffer with his staff officers pored over the maps spread out on the mahogany table. Hauptmann Weine with the ingenious mind was making little jabs at the line of forts which ran round Metz from Fort Alvensleben on the east to Fort Zastrif on the west.

"We can always fall back to the Rhine," he said jauntily. He was in that frame of mind.

"We go in somewhere here," said his colonel, and his finger covered the area of Belfort down to the south-east in Alsace.

At nine o'clock the following morning the first American reconnaissance aeroplane passed over the road that runs south to Altkirch but it was flying too high for anyone unaccustomed to identifying enemy aircraft to make certain who it might be. The 30th Division were used to Shturmoviks but not to American Mitchells. There was no doubting the unfriendly intentions of the two sections of Mitchells which came into a low level attack twenty minutes later. They scored a direct hit on the leading double-decker bus, and the next but one and nearly a platoon of No. 1 Company instantly became casualties. The second bus slewed across the road and caused a block, but all of Sasha's platoon and No. 2 Platoon of his company managed to struggle out of their vehicles and take cover in the adjacent fields while the attack lasted. When they regained the road the buses which had contained the leading company fell back in the convoy while their casualties were attended to and No. 2 Company found itself in the lead. By ten o'clock the two leading platoons had passed through Altkirch and were disembarking from their buses in a village just south of the town. Nobody seemed to know precisely where they were nor what was supposed to be taking place. The remainder of the company together with the rest of the battalion were at least ten miles to the rear.

The village appeared deserted and they passed through without seeing anyone but an old woman who with the fearlessness or indifference of old age, hobbled across the main street without a glance in their direction. Beyond the village the wooded hills rose on either side of the road and a church spire in the bend of the valley betrayed yet another village a couple of miles ahead. They left the road and took up a position in a field on the right. Here, said Lieutenant Litzmann was "the line." Ianka Valoda winked at Sasha as they lay down with their gun. Nobody attempted to dig in and Lieutenant Litzmann said that there wasn't time.

It seemed to Sasha that there was a very great deal of time. It had never stopped raining, and like the rest of them he was wet through and becoming disgusted with the turn of events. Beyond one or two sporadic skirmishes with the Partisans round Vesoul there had been little but bad food, mutiny and disgruntlement. He was probably lucky to be still alive, thanks to Sergeant Karol, but the weather was appalling and likely to grow worse. Moreover, he had an uneasy feeling that the weeks of anti-paratroop training were going to prove quite useless.

The division was intended to deal with an enemy behind the front line in the way they had operated around Radzimichy in the early days. Then recently they had been trained to deal with similar lightly armed troops. Now, without a moment's notice they had been flung into the front line. He wouldn't be at all surprised if presently they weren't faced with tanks and heavy armour. If so, God help them!

The machine-gun battle suddenly broke out over the bluff of the high hill on the right. He heard at first the smooth sewing-machine rhythm of the German weapons and then the slower "pop-pop-pop" of the American Brownings in reply. The rain stopped and the clouds began to lift. Very soon the sun might break through. He wondered if there were still leaves on the trees.

The sound of the battle increased but there was still nobody in sight. It was an uncomfortable feeling, hearing all that hullabaloo on the flank and nothing to watch but a long road winding down a sodden valley. The sun came out and fell on the distant spire so that it gleamed like white marble against the retreating cloudwrack. If it wasn't for the Spandaus and the Brownings — and they seemed strangely incongruous — it could have been a remarkably peaceful scene.

The first violent and astonishing salvo of firing from the enemy mortars fell short, but the air was immediately filled with splinters and clods of flying earth. Ianka cranked his gun and said:

"God Almighty! Where did that lot come from?"

There was still not a soul in sight. Sasha lifted the belt to bring it level with the feed. He lay on Ianka's left. Ales with the ammunition, and Hans as sharpshooter, were just to the rear. There were three other guns in the section, but no one was opening fire because there was no one at whom to aim.

The second salvo fell wide to the left, but the next dropped plumb on the flanking gun team. Earth and splinters and lumps of flesh went into the air. Lieutenant Litzmann began to swear as if he were demented. There were a dozen puffs of smoke over the village behind them and a dozen resounding explosions as the second enemy mortar battery opened fire. Flames began to flicker in the roof of several buildings and black smoke arose. Sasha wondered if the old woman would get out of this trouble alive.

The armoured cars came into sight round the bend in the road near the distant church spire. They were French cars; he recognized them from the identification lectures and charts which they had been given at Mussik. They came down the road at a steady pace. Then, as if they were satisfied that they had gauged the strength of the opposition, they drew into the hedges and opened fire, awaiting their supports. The mortar fire increased and machine-guns opened up from the wood. In his mind's eye Sasha pictured the road behind the van of the enemy's advance packed with thunderous tanks and hordes of infantry. He began to grow afraid.

The battle was developing rapidly. Ianka worked his gun with his steel helmet crammed down over his forehead while the sweat trickled down from his temples, and Ales passed the loaded belts, while Sasha fed the gun. Three of the French armoured cars had crept up under cover and were opening in enfilade. To his surprise Sasha saw, as they momentarily came into view, that the crews were swarthy and dark. They were the savage and magnificent French Moroccan troops, the "goumiers" of the First French Army. A minute later two mortar salvos and a prolonged burst of machine gun fire from the wood accounted for half the remaining German force. Lieutenant Litzmann gave a howl of dismay, unaccountably pounced upon Ianka's gun, literally tore it out of his hands, and hugging it to his belly began to run blindly back towards the burning village. Ianka started after him and Hans followed at his heels. Ales turned to Sasha with a fatuous grin of dismay and then his head suddenly dropped on to his extended forearm, and his blood and brains splattered his sleeve.

Sasha lay very still by his dead friend and he knew that if he was to survive it would be by his own doing and his alone. Any decision to be made would be his. There would be no orders to obey, no discussion amongst themselves. He kept close to the ground because the bullets were humming over his back. When there was a pause between the bursts, he knew he would get up and run after the others. But he wouldn't run blindly like that fool Lieutenant Litzmann. He would dodge and swerve and drop again when the fire became too hot. He felt that his fear was making him very cautious and more clever than he would be in ordinary circumstances. He scrambled to his feet at the first lull. A rapid glance over his shoulder showed him a road cluttered with vehicles and troops disgorging into the fields on either side. It was all very confused and not at all clear in his mind, and he knew that if afterwards he had to give an accurate description of what was happening that he wouldn't be able to do so. He dropped again as the air seemed to grow thick with bullets, then after an interval, slipping and slithering in the muddy grass, he went on once more and gained the road nearer the village and where it turned a corner. In a little time he was in the outskirts.

The main body of the battalion was arriving. Ten miles back they had cleared the roadblock and maybe now the advance could be held. Sasha, leaning against a door post, screened by a cottage porch, his hand to his heaving side, saw Sergeant Karol at the head of his platoon, moving resolutely forward, his men strung out in file behind him. There was a flickering of flame from the buildings on either side of the street, and every now and again burning timber would fall.

Sergeant Karol's platoon went past and a salvo of shells fell just behind them. Sasha darted out into the street before the second salvo should arrive. The first sounded more like field guns than mortars. He supposed in the end they would bring up something still heavier and blast them all to hell. It was getting too much of a good thing. Then he saw Ianka.

He was sitting under cover of a broken wall opposite, with Hans huddled beside him, his long, forlorn face smeared with grime, and his spectacles hanging from one ear and his rifle across his knee. The machine-gun was back in Ianka's arms which were clasped around it, almost in the same way as Lieutenant Litzmann's had been. Sasha, after a hurried glance to right and left, ran across the road and joined them.

"Oh! it's you," said Ianka. "I'm glad you're all right. Where's Ales?"

"Dead," said Sasha.

"God blast this bloody war," said Ianka. "God blast it for all its bloody, silly senselessness. Who the hell are we fighting and what are we fighting for?"

"Why ask me?" said Sasha.

There was a familiar ring about the trend of the conversation.

"We'd better have Hans here now as our Number Three," said Ianka. "What do you say to that, Hans?"

"I'm damned if I care," said Hans.

"Where's the Herr Lieutenant?" said Sasha.

"Gone to the devil, I hope," said Ianka. "But I got my gun back. I don't think he knew he had it. Completely lost his head. As a matter of fact, he's down in the back of the village now where they've formed a temporary headquarters in a cellar. He ought to feel safe down there. What happened to Ales?"

"Shot through the head, I think," said Sasha.

"How are you feeling yourself?"

"I'm all right," said Sasha. "Never say die."

"What's that?"

"Nothing. Just an old saying we used to have in the old days." The old days! Ten months ago. It wasn't a year yet. It felt like a century.

"Come on," said Ianka, struggling to his feet. "We'd better find somebody we know to report to."

The battalion dug in for the night of the nineteenth in a line of foxholes, on either side of the main street. In the village itself they occupied the few buildings that had escaped the flames. Sasha and the other two members of his machine-gun crew found Lieutenant Litzmann in his cellar and reported to him. The Herr Lieutenant hadn't seemed interested and had waved them aside. He had accepted Ales' death as of no consequence. Later Sasha remarked on their officer's indifference.

"Why should he care, the ugly brute?" said Ianka. "As far as he is concerned we're only so much rubbish. We're the brothers and cousins of mutineers, while he is in the grand tradition, the dirty rat."

They crouched in their fox-hole under the scanty shelter of their "plandecke" and the rain fell ceaselessly. There was no sound or sign of the enemy. A strange and deadly inertia seemed to have overtaken both sides. Dawn came into the sky, grey and drenched. Half-an-hour after first light Colonel Shaeffer ordered the battalion to advance. Their objective was the next village whose church spire Sasha had seen against the sky.

They took the place easily. The small number of French troops occupying it fled at sight of them. It was a large village on a slope, with ploughland on the right and meadows on the left. They dug in and awaited events. An hour after first light a Wehrmacht driver volunteered to go forward on a reconnaissance to the next village. He returned to report that the French were in occupation and that he had been fired upon. The entire division began its advance on a ten mile front. It was ten o'clock of the morning of 20 November.

Three quarters of an hour later Sasha was eating apples in the third village down the road. There seemed an endless array of little hamlets which appeared peaceful enough, though the enemy could be lurking in any of them, but the apples were juicy and sweet and Sasha was thirsty. Ianka and Hans stood munching beside him. The rain had stopped and the sun was coming out. For some extraordinary reason battle and sudden death seemed a long way off. And that, he told himself, was the way it went, rain or shine, peace or all hell let loose. The young girl with her basket was offering another apple. He took it, as much to show his appreciation as anything else and pinched her cheek. He had no wish to hurt her feelings because she looked a gentle and kindly little creature who reminded him of Valia, and who, by rights as a Frenchwoman, should be hating the Germans and anyone who had anything to do with them. He started to polish the apple on his thigh as the first shot rang out from the window of the house opposite. Hans gave a yelp of pain and clapped a hand to his shoulder. Then all three of them leapt for the doorway of the cottage by which they were standing. The door was luckily open. It had indeed been left ajar by the child who having successfully baited her trap, had disappeared with astonishing agility.

The volley seemed to be the signal for a general counter-attack. Two French tanks appeared at the far corner of the street and opened up. There was no alternative but to fall back on their former position. Somewhere, Sasha supposed, at the back of the line — if this confused intermingling of friend and foe could be so designated — the General with his staff would be assuring each other that the situation was fluid but that they had it under control. As far as he was concerned he was hourly becoming more indifferent to the outcome. Ianka's bitter words on the news of Ales' death were sinking deep. It had to be little Ales, of course, with his rosy-red cheeks, like the apples that they had been betrayed into eating. Who would have thought that a girl with yellow hair would have done a thing like that? But anybody could do anything in war.

By two o'clock they had prepared positions behind the houses and in basements for street-fighting but nobody came to challenge them, so after bandaging the flesh-wound on Hans' shoulder and on Lieutenant Litzmann's orders, since he had emerged from his cellar, they went forward to a cross-roads and opened fire on the village they had formerly occupied and which was now in the hands of the French. It seemed at the time to Sasha a foolhardy move, since once before they had stirred up a hornets' nest. This time the effect was not only instantaneous but doubly vicious and they were forced to fall back again. Thereafter till dusk there was a lull in the storm, so that Sasha must picture the situation as a gigantic game of double blind-man's buff amongst the houses, woods and meadows, with two blind giants groping for one another in a chaos of rubble and mud.

At dusk the French attacked again, and the Wehrmacht sent up an armoured car in support, but a Sherman tank which came down the road firing as it advanced scored a direct hit, and the armoured car went up in flames and smoke. The crew clambered out and yelled for bazookas, because the Sherman had momentarily withdrawn. The German crew returned to the attack and Sasha saw them go from his position in the gutter level grating of a basement. He kept thinking of Ales and Valia and the girl with the apples, so that at times it was difficult to sort out what was actual and what was day-dreaming, because everything was so inextricably confused. Then he saw the Sherman coming out of hiding and firing on the houses again, but there was no sign of the armoured car crew, so that it was only too easy to imagine what had happened to them.

The three of them scrambled out of their basement only just in time and bolted down the road with the Sherman rumbling after them. Ianka stumbled and they thought he had twisted his ankle, but he held the gun safe and found he could limp on, and then they were out in the fields again and off the road.

The Sherman snapped and barked and went out of sight, but now the battle was raging again and everywhere there seemed to be isolated groups of men firing wildly and in different directions. They had lost Lieutenant Litzmann and had seen no one in their platoon. Ianka said that wasn't surprising as they'd probably all been killed long ago, because the fight had been going on all day and they had been in the thick of it; but they met a dispatch rider that Hans had known and he told them the division was drawing out because the attack had failed. They argued amongst themselves in the falling dusk as to how the failure had come about, because it seemed that to date the honours were even, but it appeared that such indeed was the case because when they reached the village with the spire the enemy was in part possession of it and in the darkness they nearly stumbled into the trap. But they heard the sound of French voices in time and made a detour till, surprisingly, they overtook the survivors of No. 3 Company, which Sasha remembered was Sergeant Karol's.

They joined forces, plodding across the sodden fields in the darkness, and came in time to the first of the villages which had been their starting point at ten o'clock that morning and found themselves amongst friends again. Then they put themselves under the orders of a German sergeant and he posted them to a small hill overlooking the road and just beyond the first row of cottages. Having dug themselves in to the depth of a small gun-pit, they collapsed, exhausted. They had consumed all their rations and were growing very hungry. At eleven o'clock that night the enemy barrage suddenly set the ground trembling beneath them.

The opening salvos burst two hundred yards in front of their position. The shelling increased to drum-fire pitch, then lifted and descended again, two hundred yards behind. Had the barrage been accurate there would have been few survivors of the battalion in their shallow fox-holes. Shelling continued all night. Sasha peering into the darkness strained to catch that first dark movement against darkness that could be the warning of an approaching attack, but none came.

Just before dawn on 26 November seven German Mark V Panther tanks crept into the village that straddled the line. So cautiously and silently did they reach their positions that their presence was disclosed only when they opened fire on the enemy-occupied village down the road. Two miles to the rear the German artillery opened up simultaneously in support and the battalion went into the attack on the heels of the barrage. On the outskirts of the village the assault was held up and the German shells, falling short, came down on their own men. As they lay in the fields ready to go forward the legionnaires of the 30 Ost Division were partially destroyed by their ally's guns.

Colonel Shaeffer was killed, and Captain Weine almost immediately died of his wounds. The casualties amongst other ranks were over fifty per cent. The battle lasted all day. Towards mid-afternoon six Panthers circling outside the village encountered the French Shermans on the right flank. Only one tank survived the engagement. At four o'clock, unable to hold the positions without the support of their armour, the battalion fell back on to their original position. They immediately dug in, mined the road and, mauled and maimed, crawled back to their fox-holes to lick their wounds. On 29 November orders arrived to withdraw through Altkirch to Schlettstadt, which town they had left thirteen days before. The battalion had lost its beloved and gallant commanding officer, a brilliant second-in-command, nearly half its establishment of officers, commissioned and non-commissioned, and a high percentage of its rank and file.

Sasha sat by the roadside on the way back to Schlettstadt while the battalion rested for the customary ten minutes' interval. Everyone had been told, or at least the story had got round, that they were only retreating to shorten the line and so strengthen it. Somehow that statement again seemed to have a familiar ring about it. They had retired through Altkirch and been given a trouncing by the Allied artillery as they had passed through the town. The Americans and the French were pressing on fast. There had been plenty of Germans in Altkirch and most of them had still seemed pretty confident. Maybe, Sasha thought it was the only way they dared allow themselves to think. Maybe that was it.

The whistle went to "fall in" and he got stiffly to his feet. He was footsore and the food was still almost uneatable, so that he felt famished and weak. Maybe he'd feel better if the old days and the old companions could come back just for an hour or so, he told himself, with Mikita calling him "little rascal" and chuckling over his vodka; with Symon trotting along by his side and Paval in the next file. Only Paval lay outstretched before the pill-boxes by the River Dvina and Symon sprawled in a welter of blood and limbs near a far-distant wood in another land. Maybe, if Kurt was here he'd feel better, but Kurt lay huddled in a gas-chamber, and Ales sprawled dead with his head blown in; maybe if Major Shaeffer were saluting him again on the square at Lomza and about to shake him by the hand, maybe then he'd feel better. Or if Nicola could be here or even if he himself could be near home at Haradischa. Home! Would he ever see home again?

He lifted up his chin and squared his shoulders. He was an old soldier, and it was no part of a veteran to repine.

"Never say die," he said to himself.

But the words seemed to stick in his throat and choke him.

4

They had been here now in the vicinity of the Haut-Konisburg on the 2,483 foot mountain spur of the Vosges Forest for over a week, having passed through Schlettstadt on the way to Rapoltsveiler. That is to say one company of the battalion composed of the combined survivors of the four original companies had made their way up the mountain to hold the roadblocks of massive trees which the Wehrmacht had built over the main road and to relieve the German troops, who had pulled out exhausted. All the rest of the division had been sent across the Rhine to regroup. On a fine day Sasha could see across the great river to the mountains that lay in Germany itself.

Lieutenant Litzmann was here and so were Sergeants Karol and Webber and some eighteen others. Ianka still handled his gun, now replaced by the heavier "42," and Hans' shoulder had healed. They had reinforced the former roadblock which was a stockade of great trees and which the Germans had felled, with further timbers, and then constructed gun-sites and footholds higher up the hill on the steep slope for themselves. Both sides of the vital main road were covered by the concentrated fire of the company who now awaited events. It was the first week in December and the Americans were fast advancing.

On the fourth day the American tanks came up the mountain road to the attack. Sasha was the first to hear them distinctly and with any degree of certainty, since it was purely a question of contrasting a greater noise against many small ones, in the same way as a soldier learnt to see in the dark. All day there had been heavy gun fire and the sound of tank battles on either side, but there had been no particular movement on their sector. Now someone was tapping at the front door; soon he would be pounding his way in.

The roadblock was well over six feet high and proportionately solid, composed of great tree trunks, lashed together and in some places walled with boulders. On either side the magnificent forest converged close to the road, though a track on the right led to the crest of the splendid hill. The continuous bombardment of their positions pinned the company down to their gun-positions and kept them in a constant state of watchfulness. Sasha and his gun were sited some way down the slope and relatively near the barrier. Having helped in its reconstruction he was confident that it would take some considerable forcing. It was a comforting, reassuring kind of front door; unless of course somebody should leave the back door open!

The Shermans came up the road and halted at the obstruction. There were three of them in line, each covering the other. There was no sense in opening fire on them because there was a shortage of anti-tank guns and the roadblock would serve its purpose. Moreover if there were infantry as far up as this in support of the armour, they would scarcely venture to by-pass the obstruction and leave their tanks. On the other hand, since one guess was as good as another, anything could happen.

Nothing happened. No infantry appeared advancing between the close-set trees over the mountain side, and after a little time all three tanks trundled round on their tracks and lumbered off the way they had come. An hour later the inevitable reconnaissance aeroplane, flying very low to invite enemy fire, passed over the tree-tops. Again nobody opened fire, refusing to disclose the position. Night began to fall and though there was constant evidence of heavy fighting continuing on either side, no attempt was made to force the roadblock. That in one sense could be very gratifying since it implied a hearty respect for the strength of the barricade, but in another sense it could be a little disquieting.

Moreover they were getting very hungry indeed. There had never been an issue of iron rations, and their issue rations had not reached them. Sasha and Ianka and Hans sat at their gun-site and listened to the receding sounds of battle. After a little time Hans took off his glasses, wiped them with a very dirty handkerchief, replaced them, and looked at his companion lugubriously over the rims. They could just see one another in the dusk.

"If you care to ask me," said Hans, "We are in the process of being abandoned."

"And so?" said Ianka.

"We shall not know till tomorrow's dawn unless the enemy fights all through the night, which I am doubtful about," continued Hans portentously. "And so if the noise dies down out on the right and left, it may be because both sides are holding their fire and without that noise we have no means of judging what's happening. What will you do if our gallant allies, if the Herrenvolk betray us, again, Sasha Nioman?"

Farther up the slope somebody else in the encroaching darkness seemed to be sharing similar views and expressing them with indiscretion. Lieutenant Litzmann was addressing Sergeant Karol.

"We should have orders to fall back by now. What is the good of holding on when the flanks are giving way?"

"There is still time for a message to get through," was the reply.

The sound of Sergeant Karol's voice, clear and familiar in the cold dank air reached Sasha and comforted him. It was good to think that Sergeant Karol was nearby, he always inspired confidence, which was more than could be said for Lieutenant Litzmann. There might of course be something in Hans' view, yet on the other hand what did anybody know about anything? But this, since it came from a slightly higher authority, might be worth listening to. Sasha kept his ears strained through the darkness.

"I shall never permit myself to suffer the indignity of being taken a prisoner of war." It was Lieutenant Litzmann speaking again. "No. No. I shall shoot myself first. I shall not surrender."

"Do you think it wise, Herr Lieutenant," replied Sergeant Karol, "to talk in that vein so loudly? Somebody may be listening."

"When I need a sergeant to advise me I will broadcast the fact."

The Lieutenant was clearly indignant.

"Just as you wish."

The contempt in Sergeant Karol's voice was only too apparent. It was remarkable what degree of "dumb insolence" could be inferred by the slightest inflection. Lieutenant Litzmann was not slow in noticing it. He immediately took offence.

"When we get back to base, Sergeant Karol —"

"When we get back, Herr Lieutenant!" Sergeant Karol spoke curtly. "It's my opinion —" He broke off short. "I think we are talking too much, sir."

Twenty yards away in the darkness Sasha was telling himself that a month ago Sergeant Karol would never have dared to air such views before a senior officer. And yet Sergeant Karol was still a good soldier and a first rate N.C.O. Something must have happened to him to have allowed him to permit himself such a liberty.

At dawn the men began to leave their gun-sites and gather in small groups, despite the warning shouts of their officers and N.C.O.s to remain at their posts. The shelling had long since ceased and the great wooded slopes seemed singularly silent. Far off, and ominously from the rear and in the direction of Rapoltsveiler, came the dull rumble of a continuous cannonade, but it sounded to be several valleys away.

By eleven o'clock, forty-eight hours had elapsed without proper rations, and the relief that should have arrived had been instructed to withdraw. Something very clearly had gone wrong. Imperceptibly but nevertheless quite definitely, discipline was slackening. The general anxiety was beginning to erase the distinguishing marks of rank; men and officers fraternized and nobody seemed to be prepared to assume his rightful responsibility. And now farther still to the east behind Rapoltsveiler came the muttering of the guns.

At noon Sasha went up, through the trees, to the mountain top. He took Hans with him, leaving Ianka in charge of the machine-gun. He could see the figure of Sergeant Karol ahead and knew that if he had the chance he would speak with him. He could feel the barriers of custom and routine were down, and he knew that the sergeant would talk sense.

Hans stalked along with a stride that left Sasha breathless, but they were reaching more open ground, the rocky tableland that formed the summit, when a burst of rifle-fire took them by surprise.

This reminder of the enemy's presence came out of the blue in a quick succession of rifle shots that whined across the plateau, and when they struck a stone, ricocheted off with the drone of a spinning top. Hans and Sasha dropped flat to the ground and Sergeant Karol came running back to them. He dropped down beside them. He was grinning all over his face and the little gold flecks in his eyes danced like sparks.

"Well, that proves it," he said, and his grin grew wider.

"Proves what, sergeant?" asked Hans. The corners of his mouth were drawn down and he looked as if he could cry.

"They've got behind us."

"Who's got behind us?" said Hans.

"The enemy, you damn fool," said Sergeant Karol. "Those shots came from over there."

He pointed across the deep valley to the distant ridge that ran from north to south.

"We're cut off!" said Sasha.

"Yes, my little 'kutscher'," said Sergeant Karol. "We're cut off and surrounded and bloody well done for unless we cut our way out. Let's get down the hill and spread the glad tidings."

"It's just what I thought would happen," wailed Hans. "Just what I thought. Oh God, what fools they've made of us!"

Down by the barricades and the gun-sites they had heard the sound of rifle fire and had already guessed its significance. Lieutenant Litzmann and Sergeant Weber were coming up the mountain side to meet them as they came down.

"They've got behind us," said Sergeant Karol to the Lieutenant. There was a vicious glint in his eye. "You'd better get your pistol out, sir, if you don't want to be taken prisoner."

"They'll never take me," said Lieutenant Litzmann. "But God in Heaven, what shall we do?"

"That's up to you," said Sergeant Karol. "You're the senior officer here."

"How near are they?" demanded the Lieutenant. "How many of them are there?"

"I don't know, about half a million, at a rough guess," said Sergeant Karol, "and under the mile, I should think. I was only interested in the direction from which they opened fire. That told me all I wanted to know."

"This is terrible," said Lieutenant Litzmann.

Sergeant Karol exchanged glances with Sergeant Weber. The latter gave a significant shrug of disdain. It seemed that Sergeant Karol was not alone in his views of their senior officer. Hans, without warning, suddenly sank to the ground and began to blubber.

"Oh, for God's sake, shut up," said Sasha and attempted to pull the other to his feet.

"If you ask me, Herr Lieutenant," said Sergeant Weber, "It might be a good idea to hold a conference with your platoon commanders. And then when you've decided what to do, you can tell the men. I don't think I should waste much time," he added.

Lieutenant Litzmann called a conference. There was the one officer and twenty German sergeants present. They stood in a group at the foot of a towering fir tree and the Lieutenant harangued them in vehement undertones. Once or twice someone would interrupt him and several times he smote one fist into the palm of his other hand. Sasha, watching from the gun-site where he'd joined Ianka thought it must be a very stormy meeting with the Lieutenant, as usual, losing his head.

"This is bad," said Ianka. "I don't know how it could be worse. What have you done with Hans?"

"Left him farther up the hill blubbing like a baby."

"Poor fool," said Ianka.

At noon the conference dispersed and the German sergeants rejoined their platoons and told the men of the situation and the decision that had been reached. The enemy forces, so their story went, had by-passed their position and their own supporting flanks had fallen back without letting anyone know of their intention. The three tanks that had approached the roadblocks the day before and had turned back had clearly decided that the roadblock was too formidable to force and had determined to find another way round. The enemy had clearly advanced beyond this position because at eleven o'clock this morning a party of their own men had been fired on from a ridge three quarters of a mile to the rear. Nevertheless the enemy lines would not be stabilized at the moment and therefore it might be possible to penetrate them under cover of darkness and so overtake the main German lines as they retreated. That then, was the situation, which was admittedly desperate. The decision that had been reached, however, was that for the one hundred and eighty legionnaires who comprised the rank and file of the company, it should be from now on every man for himself. They could consider themselves free to move at this moment, singly or in parties; but the German sergeants, senior sergeants and their one officer, would form a party of their own which would be separate from the legionnaires.

Lieutenant Litzmann, making a round of his gun-sites in person to impart this cheerful information, was insistent on the necessity of the Germans and their allies moving off in separate parties but gave no reason. On Litzmann's departure from his particular gun-site, Ianka Valoda, suspecting treachery and wishing to express his opinion, spat after him. The officer wheeled round, drew his automatic, and fired two rounds into the pit of the machine-gunner's stomach. Before he died in Sasha's arms, Ianka said:

"Be on your guard, Sasha. They will betray you yet."

Sasha laid Ianka out with his hands folded over his chest and spread his "plandecke" over his face. Then with the dead man lying two yards away he sat with his back against a tree. He had no idea what course he would pursue or what his fate might be. He only knew that as a unit the last company of the 30th Division to remain in occupied territory had ceased to exist.

It began to rain a steady downpour that threshed through the trees. In a little time a small puddle had formed in a hollow of the "plandecke" that covered Ianka. As time passed the puddle became a pool and overflowed. Sasha, crouching against the streaming tree, watched the water trickling down on to the corpse's limp hand that lay upturned with outspread fingers. He supposed he ought to cover Ianka's hand, but he couldn't be bothered to move. Nor could he be bothered to think. This must surely be the end.

A great sense of weariness overcame him. He felt that he was so tired that he would never move again. The brutal murder of Ianka had shocked him as much as anything he had experienced. He could think of the act as nothing less than murder. He wondered where Hans might be and found that he couldn't care if Hans were dead or alive. People were moving about the wood in twos and threes. They were breaking up, scattering — "every man for himself." He supposed that he too should make up his mind and try and find a way through this maze of trees, over the great hills and ravines, and hope for the best. He was so tired and hungry that he felt beyond hope.

"Wake up," said the voice of Sergeant Karol. "Pull yourself together, 'kutscher'."

Sasha looked up and saw that dark, clean-cut face with its brazen, dancing eyes, glinting down at him. He felt for some unknown reason suddenly ashamed of himself.

"Never say 'die'," said Sergeant Karol. "Wasn't that what you lads used to say? Well, now's the time to say it."

Sasha nodded. It seemed that Sergeant Karol with those cat's eyes of his could see into the darkness of another man's soul.

"Now listen to me," said Sergeant Karol, taking a seat beside him. "Some of us are going to get out of this, but what I tell you, you must keep to yourself. It's not to be passed on to any of the others. Is that understood?"

"Certainly it is," said Sasha.

"Very well then. At dusk, just on twenty of us, the German sergeants and the Lieutenant are going to meet secretly by the roadblock. We've made the meeting for five o'clock. We shall move off immediately and I am to be in charge of the party. They've elected me to that honour." He gave a short laugh. "It seems that in an emergency the master-race doesn't always lead. Our intention is to catch up with the Wehrmacht wherever they are making a stand. It can't be a very great distance away, but we shall have to pass through the American lines to reach the Germans. It's going to be tricky, but it's an organized attempt to escape which is more than you can say has been suggested by any of the others. The rest of you legionnaires can look after yourselves. The Germans as usual are walking out on you. You can think what you like, but if you yourself like to come down to the roadblock and meet us there at five o'clock you can join us."

"Thank you," said Sasha. "You're my guardian angel, aren't you, Sergeant Karol? I owe you my life once already."

"Keep your chin up," said Sergeant Karol. "At five o'clock then, and not a word to anyone."

It was raining more heavily than ever at the appointed time. Rivulets of water were trickling down the slope, between the boulders and stones, as Sasha made his way to the barricade. In the dusk he could see a dozen or more men gathered together and he recognized Sergeant Weber and Lieutenant Litzmann at once. He couldn't discuss Sergeant Karol amongst the others. He approached the group with some diffidence and stopped dead in his tracks, when the Lieutenant, noticing him, shouted over Sergeant Weber's shoulder:

"What are you doing here?"

Sergeant Weber swung round and his face went dark with anger.

"Get away from here," he said to Sasha. "We want nothing to do with you. You've had explicit instructions. You don't belong to us. Join your own people."

Lieutenant Litzmann drew his automatic pistol.

"Clear away out of this," he said. "Else I'll give you some of what I gave your friend."

A third figure moved beside the Lieutenant, emerging from the little crowd of men.

"Not so fast, Herr Lieutenant," said Sergeant Karol. "Put that toy of yours away. It might go off."

"This man had my personal instructions that he was not to join us," said Lieutenant Litzmann furiously. "I had to shoot the gunner for mutinous behaviour —"

"He's here on *my* invitation," said Sergeant Karol. "He's an old friend."

"Well, we don't want him. If we take one of them along with us, then all the others will want to come. What chance would we stand then?"

"Nevertheless," said Sergeant Karol. "He's coming with us."

"And what if I say 'no'?"

"Then I shall say to you, Herr Lieutenant, 'Go to hell'."

"You dare to speak to me like that."

"I certainly dare. If my friend doesn't join our party, then neither do I. You've elected me to get you out of this trouble, but if you are so clever you can get yourselves out and find your way alone, Sasha and I will go on our own. You can take it or leave it, it's all the same to me."

"Oh, let the little beast come along," said Sergeant Weber. "We'll have the whole place about our ears in a minute and then we shall be properly in the soup. Those brutes outnumber us by ten to one."

The party led by Sergeant Karol left the roadblock at a quarter past five. Sasha kept the leader company while the remainder followed in single file as they made their way down the steep slope. No one saw them go, for the remainder of the legionnaires who had decided to await nightfall before making their attempt to penetrate the lines were huddled together in small groups beneath the trees, sheltering from the torrential rain.

The party were armed; Sergeant Karol with a tommy-gun and pistol, Sasha with a rifle and grenade, and the rest with their customary weapons. No one carried a compass, so that Sergeant Karol must keep in his mind's eye the pictures of the terrain as viewed from the hilltop that morning. They had long since consumed the last of their rations.

They made some progress before darkness fell, but thereafter it was necessary to halt on four occasions in order to keep in touch. They sat down to rest. It was bitterly cold. The rain fell in vicious squalls, lashing across their shoulders like a whip, saturating their garments, and glueing them to their half-frozen bodies. Sasha sat beside Sergeant Karol with his teeth chattering.

"Take hold of this," said Sergeant Karol, and thrust his blanket into Sasha's lap. He himself crouched, shivering, under his "plandecke." They waited an hour and then Lieutenant Litzmann felt his way forward along the line of disconsolate and dispirited men till he found the leader.

"We shall freeze to death if we don't soon move," he said.

"Very well," said Sergeant Karol. "We'll go on again. Perhaps you would prefer to come up to the head of the column with me. Two pairs of eyes are better than one."

They spoke in whispers, for despite the sigh and moan of wind and rain, the night could still possess ears.

"No, carry on," said Lieutenant Litzmami, "I'll keep the stragglers in hand."

"And let me get the first shot as it comes," muttered Sergeant Karol to himself.

They went on again. Once they heard the distant thud of falling bombs but there was no sound of artillery fire or the crackle of small arms. High above the cloud wrack an early moon climbed into the sky. A little of its light filtered through to the party struggling on below. The man behind could now discern the outline of the fellow ahead of him. At the end of another hour Sergeant Karol stopped so suddenly that Sasha stumbled into him. The remainder of the file concertinaed into one another. There was the outline of a house immediately ahead of them.

There was no light in the high, dark rectangle of deeper darkness and they waited kneeling together in the pelting rain while Sergeant Karol explained his plan under his breath. They would wait ten minutes and then, if there was no sign of life, surround the place and then one by one creep forward converging on the building till they were once again within hand's breadth of one another. A door would certainly be found by someone and he should attempt to open it or force it. If a light went on or a challenge rang out he would immediately drop down where he was and everyone would await developments. There were three main eventualities; the house could be occupied by its legitimate owners, in which case being outnumbered they could be coerced into providing shelter; it could be in the possession of the enemy, who would disclose his identity by his native tongue, or, if they were in luck, and as the place was in the battle-area, it could have been abandoned. As Sergeant Karol elaborated his plan the moon suddenly came out in a rift of the clouds and the rain lifted. They moved off to their positions.

Sasha at Sergeant Karol's side could see the shapes of the two buildings before him quite plainly. The larger appeared to be a two storied house and alongside it a smaller building suggested a garage or stable. Sergeant Karol nudged him and they stepped forward together.

Everybody, their weapons raised in readiness, reached the house together. No one from inside had called out; no dog had barked. There was a door in front of Lieutenant Litzmann. He touched the man beside him on the shoulder and indicated the entrance. It was no part of the Lieutenant's philosophy to invite disaster. The sergeant raised his fist and hammered on the door. Utter silence prevailed. Then he tried the door-handle. It turned. He thrust the door open and passed inside. A second later the doorway leapt into being as he switched a light on. They all began to pass in, one by one. The premises had been abandoned.

"This way, I think," said a voice in Sasha's ear.

Sasha followed Sergeant Karol across a yard and toward the stables. The square of light from the open door disappeared. Nobody was taking any chances. After a rest and a little time to attempt to dry their clothes they would go on again. The moonlight was bright now, but soon it would disappear again.

The clouds were racing across the sky. The stables too were empty. They had been occupied recently because there was horse manure unswept on the cobbles of a stall. A ladder was propped against the wall and overhead was the open hatch of a loft.

"And this is the answer," said Sergeant Karol, raising the ladder to the hatch. "Follow on after me."

He went up the ladder hand over hand and crawled into the loft. He must have risen to his feet because Sasha could hear his footsteps sounding loud and hollow from above. Then Sasha went up. Outside the moonlight went out like a snuffed candle.

"Pull up the ladder," said Sergeant Karol.

Sasha could just see his companion kneeling by the edge of the hatch. Between them they hauled the ladder up and laid it on the bare boards of the floor. The air was full of dust and Sasha began to sneeze.

"Take control of that," said Sergeant Karol. "We don't want to give ourselves away."

He began to chuckle. Then he moved across the loft.

"There's some hay here." His voice sounded through the darkness. "Come and sit down. We can dry off a bit here and they'll never find us. No ladder, no loft."

Sasha crossed to him and the scent of hay greeted his nostrils. He sank down in it, his wet clothes clinging to him.

"I've had enough of this," said Sergeant Karol. "And no doubt so have you."

"It was different in Byelorussia," said Sasha.

"Something to fight for, to fight against. But not here. Shall I tell you my plan?"

"Yes," said Sasha.

"Germany can't win the war now," said Sergeant Karol. "It's only a matter of time before she collapses — and what do we owe Germany anyway? We've a lot to be thankful for, I don't think. Every time they leave us in the lurch. Even now because I'm leading them I should be the first to get shot, they saw to that. They chose me because there isn't one among them worth his salt. If they come in to look for us, and they will, don't answer. Promise me."

"Yes," said Sasha. "I promise."

"You and I will get out of this together — just you and I alone. When I reach the American lines I am going to give myself up. Then when I am a prisoner of war I shall volunteer to fight for the Polish Army as I'm a Pole."

"There's no Polish Army now," said Sasha.

"Don't be a dolt, 'kutscher.' There's a Free Polish Army that's fighting for the British, isn't there?"

The audacity of the idea took Sasha's breath away. He gasped. Sergeant Karol chuckled again in the darkness.

"And you can do the same, Sasha Nioman."

"But I'm not a Pole, I'm a Byelorussian."

"Don't be such a damn fool," said Sergeant Karol. "You want to live, don't you? Who's to say you are not a Pole if you say you are? You're not expected to carry your birth certificate round with you. As far as that goes I intend to give myself up to any of the Allied Forces as long as they are not coloured troops. Listen."

There was the sound of footsteps in the yard outside.

"They are looking for us. Not a sound," whispered Karol.

"Sergeant Karol." It was Lieutenant Litzmann's voice.

There came a crash from below as of something overturned, followed by a volley of oaths, then from the yard again another voice took up the refrain. It was Sergeant Weber's.

"Karol. Are you there?"

There was no answer from above. In the dusty silence Sasha could hear his companion's controlled breathing.

"Karol ... damn the fellow, where's he got to? We're going to move on again. It's too risky staying here. Are you there, Karol?"

"They've run off." It was the Lieutenant's voice. "The dirty rat's let us down."

"If ever I run across either of them..." said Sergeant Weber.

A door below slammed, and the footsteps faded away. In a little time there were more footsteps, and muttered orders, and once the Lieutenant's voice raised momentarily in an angry yelp.

"They're quarrelling amongst themselves," whispered Sergeant Karol in his loft, and chuckled again. From outside came the clatter of a falling billy-can and the clank of rifle butts on cobbles, then a further shuffling of footsteps, and then at last silence.

"Goodnight," said Sergeant Karol. "And — goodnight."

Sasha could hear him scratching out a bed for himself in the deep hay.

"We'll spend the night here," said Sergeant Karol. "And in the morning we'll decide on our next step. Goodnight, my 'kutscher'."

"Goodnight, Sergeant Karol," said Sasha.

Sasha lay back in the hay and the warmth of his body began to penetrate his soaking clothes. He wondered how far Lieutenant Litzmann's party had got by now and if they would ever manage to reach the Wehrmacht lines. Then he thought of how once before but oh! so long ago it just wasn't true — he had slept in a stall with Lieutenant Kubik's horse and a certain sergeant with golden, glittering eyes had come upon him during his rounds and questioned him in a strange way about his brother and how in the end it had been this same sergeant who had recommended him for a soldier. It seemed that Sergeant Karol must remember that as well since he kept on calling him "kutscher" as if to remind him of that first real meeting, in a taunting sort of way which from anyone else could be offensive. But not from Sergeant Karol.

Where now could that brother be? Oh where indeed? Only it was a great comfort to think that Nicola would have approved of Sergeant Karol, who was indeed like an elder brother, which was such a splendid thing to possess. In some sort of way which he couldn't explain, it was again like coming home to someone trusted and beloved. In that alone lay a great peace. He could hear a couple of yards away his friend's deep, steady breathing. Now and again he would grunt and mutter in his sleep, and once he called out in a strangely touching way: "Don't leave me, Marysia. I'm on my way home." Sasha wondered who Marysia might be and what hold she had over Sergeant Karol, and felt a little jealous that someone else had his friend's heart in trust since he must call out and plead with her in his sleep. It seemed that for all his tough ways this strange, hard, feckless man was after all but another child. Sasha rolled over on his side and went to sleep.

He awoke with daylight in his eyes. It was eight o'clock of the morning. His clothes still stuck to his body so that he wondered when he'd begin to breed lice. He was very hungry, but he was rested. Sergeant Karol was beginning to stir so he waited for a few minutes and then roused him.

"What the hell?" said Sergeant Karol. "Oh! yes, I remember."

He sat up coughing and spitting.

"We want to get into the house," said Sasha, "And dry off properly and find some food."

"Nothing better," said Sergeant Karol. "But we'll make a brief reconnaissance first. You listen that end, I'll take the other."

He rose cautiously to his hands and knees and crawled to the end of the loft. Sasha taking the other end did likewise. He crouched there, listening. There was no sound at all. The wind seemed to have dropped because it no longer moaned round the eaves and the rain had stopped beating on the roof.

"Very good," said Sergeant Karol. "Nothing moving. We'll chance it. Put the ladder down."

Between them they lowered the ladder and climbed down. It appeared to be quite bright sunlight outside because sunbeams threading through the chinks between the wooden planking of the stable wall pierced the interior darkness and set the motes dancing. Sasha crossed the stable and put his eye to a crack. There was, as far as his limited range of vision permitted, no one about. He could see into the yard and observed a horse trough and a pump and on the other side the corner of the house and a view of the front door which was ajar.

"It seems to me safe," he said.

Sergeant Karol applied his eye to the chink. After a minute he said: "We'll risk it. The door's half-open, so it doesn't look as if there's anyone at home."

They crossed the yard side by side and went into the house.

There was a door on the right and left and one at the end of the passage which was flanked by a staircase. The matting of the hall floor was muddied, clearly by the visitors of the night. There was no sound but the ticking of a large clock on a wall-bracket. The house could not have been long abandoned by its rightful owners. The two intruders tip-toed to the end of the corridor and listened. Sergeant Karol raised his eyebrows and shrugged his shoulders.

"Now for it," he said.

He laid his hand on the doorknob. As if he had tuned in to a wireless set a loud, reverberating and shuddering snore greeted his action. It came from the room beyond. He whipped his hand away as if it had touched red-hot iron. A broad grin overspread Sasha's face. Despite himself he began to giggle hopelessly.

"Shut up, you little fool," whispered Sergeant Karol viciously.

The snore sounded again. This time it was a mighty crescendo ending in an explosion and a grunt. Very cautiously Sergeant Karol turned the knob and opened the door. He peered into the room.

"Good God!" he said. "Look at that!"

5

Hans, erstwhile orderly room runner and member of Sasha's machine-gun crew lay flat on his back. His mouth was wide open and he was sound asleep. By his side, covered with a rug, lay a second figure.

"It's Peter Savich of my platoon," said Sergeant Karol. "Now would you believe it?"

He stood looking down at the two recumbent figures. Hans was clothed only in his shirt. His tunic and trousers with most of Peter's uniform were draped across the back of two chairs which stood before the grate of what was apparently the living-room. A fire burnt low behind the bars. Two rifles in a corner leant against the wall.

"There is nothing in this life," said Sergeant Karol loudly, "like making yourself at home."

Peter Savich suddenly sat bolt upright with his eyes open, wide awake. He was a swarthy, broad-shouldered youth with an amiable grin that was now slowly spreading across his face which had at first revealed fear.

"Hullo, sir," he said. "You put the fear of God in me for the moment. Till I saw who it was. Wake up, Hans! Wake up!"

Hans rolled over and began to rub his eyes, then he, too, sat up.

"Good God," he said. "It's Sasha! What are you doing here?"

"Same as yourself," said Sasha. "We were in the loft, but you seem to have done yourselves proud!"

"We got a fire going, there's plenty of logs in the cellar, but I don't think that there's any food left. There was only a bit of stale bread in the larder and Peter and I ate it. Take some of your clothes off and dry them."

"Have you seen anyone else?" said Sergeant Karol. "Any of the German sergeants for instance?"

He began to undress after carefully laying his tommy-gun and field-glasses on the floor.

"Not a soul," said Hans. "I'll get dressed and you can use the chair. I'll get some more firewood in a minute."

Hans brought logs from the cellar and the fire roared up the chimney. The clothes were dry within the hour.

"What are your plans?" said Sergeant Karol.

"I'm finished with this caper," said Hans. "Treating us like dirt."

He eyed his senior suspiciously.

"I suppose," he said, "You could take offence at that and try and charge me — if you ever get to an orderly room to charge me in again."

"I'm not taking offence," said Sergeant Karol. "Sasha and I are of the same opinion. We're going to hand ourselves over at the first opportunity."

"I'm going to look for some food," said Sasha.

He searched the house, both upstairs and down. There was nothing to be found but one medium-sized potato in the cellar. He wondered who had inhabited the place and why it was so bare and then came to realize that they might not have been the first and only visitors. But he proudly carried his find back to the living-room and when they had peeled it, they cooked it in a billycan and Sasha halved it with Sergeant Karol. The other two refused a share, since they had raided the larder previously.

"That wasn't enough," said Sasha. "I'm going to look round again."

"If you're going outside," said Sergeant Karol. "Leave your cap and tunic. Then if anyone spots you — and there can be scores of people about — they'll take you for a civilian."

"You think of everything," said Sasha.

He left his jacket and cap on the chair. He was beginning to admire Sergeant Karol more than ever. Little things and big things, they were all alike to him, such as saving a man from the gas-chamber or sharing a morsel of potato with him. It was more than ever like having an elder brother again.

He went down the passage cautiously and peered out of the front door. It was going to be a fine day after the icy deluge of rain in the night. He could see from the porch the outspread panorama of the splendid wooded hills and, with the visibility excellent in the cold rain-drenched air, the far-off glimmer of reflected light which was the Rhine. If Sergeant Karol were right — and, of course, he was! — it wouldn't be long now before the German armies had been driven across to the other side.

There was a small orchard immediately opposite the house, and as there was no sign of anyone about, he went down the garden path and climbed the fence that went round the trees like a paddock. Surprisingly for the time of year there were several apples left on one or two trees. He collected half a dozen of them and returned to the house.

"They're not much," he said. "But it's something. I saw an outhouse across the yard, and I'll go and see what's doing there."

"Keep your eyes open," warned Sergeant Karol and munched his apple.

The outhouse was filled with gardening tools, but on a shelf by a cobwebbed window he found a narrow-necked, earthenware gallon jar, and on the window-ledge what appeared a small bag of meal. There was a yellowish white substance like lard in the jar and he scooped out a lump of the stuff on the end of a stick. Ravenous, he thrust it into his mouth. It was tallow, and he spat it out hurriedly and turned his attention a trifle more cautiously to the meal. He was disappointed to discover by a similar method that it was scouring powder for pots and pans, nor was he successful in finding one solitary scrap of food though he searched everywhere. Then he went back to the house.

"No luck," he said.

Sergeant Karol had put his uniform on. All their clothes had dried out by now. He picked up his field-glasses and slung them round his neck.

"You and I," he said to Sasha, "Will make a reconnaissance and find out the lie of the land."

He turned and led the way out.

"What we want to know," he said, "is the present position of our own people and the others. I don't want to walk into the German lines, my mind's made up."

The road to Rapoltsveiler ran over a ridge less than a quarter of a mile from the house. Side by side they made their way along it. In many places it had been torn up by tanks' tracks and pools of muddy water had formed, but the morning was still clear and fine. The ground was steeply rising on either side of the road, and when they reached the crest they climbed on to the higher ground and Sergeant Karol took out his glasses.

Rapoltsveiler lay beneath them a mile and a half away. From this height they could almost see into the streets. Sergeant Karol focused his glasses and kept them steady on his eyes as he scanned the scene before him. There was no sound at all of battle.

"Take a look. I can't see any movements," said Sergeant Karol and handed the glasses over.

There was no sign of human activity amidst the houses of the town below nor in the hills surrounding it. Then as he was about to pass the glasses back Sasha caught sight of a slight movement over the hedge which skirted the road at a corner not a hundred yards ahead of where they stood.

He watched intently and within seconds the figure of a man could be seen walking briskly in their direction.

"There's somebody coming up the road," he said. "Have a look for yourself."

"It looks like a Frenchman," said Sergeant Karol a moment later. "It's a civilian at any rate. That will suit our purpose."

They went down the bank and waited by the side of the road. As the stranger came nearer Sasha could see he was a middle-aged man with a muffler round his neck and a beret on his head. He came swinging along the road whistling as he approached. The tune died on his lips as Sergeant Karol hailed him.

He stopped abruptly and for one moment Sasha thought he was about to turn and run, but he came on slowly, a frown on his face, and his hands plunged deep into his trouser pockets.

"Rapoltsveiler?" said Sergeant Karol, pointing to the distant town.

"*Oui, oui,*" replied the peasant and broke into a torrent of French.

"We'll have to make him understand by signs," said Sasha.

He plucked at the man's sleeve. There were one or two words he had acquired in the days of his Haradischa schooling and he had augmented them with a few he learnt in his short period of service. He pointed to the town.

"*Allemands?*" He jabbed significantly with his finger.

"*Non, non.*" The Frenchman shook his head vigorously. "*Américains.*"

He began to gesture, making signs of a struggle. It was quite clear what had happened. The German lines were now still farther to the east towards the Rhine and the Americans were in possession of Rapoltsvieler. Thereafter their exchange of signs became more explicit and comprehensible.

Certainly, they were given to understand, the town was occupied by the American forces. Scores of Germans had surrendered. There was food in plenty if they were hungry. Did they wish to give themselves up? Would he return to the house with them where they had left their arms and two of their companions? Certainly he would and then if they liked, he would guide them down into Rapoltsveiler, because, of course from their uniforms, he knew them for what they were.

The three of them went back to the house together. Sasha wondered what Colonel Shaeffer, who had shaken him by the hand, and Captain Weine would have thought of this decision to lay down their arms. But the Colonel and the Captain were dead men, while people like Lieutenant Litzmann and all the others of his kidney lived on. He stole a glance at Sergeant Karol. There was no sign of any queasy conscience on that handsome face but rather a bitter and defiant look, so that when Sergeant Karol caught his eye and flashed a brilliant smile, Sasha knew that whatever anybody else might think, that he himself was on Sergeant Karol's side and that as long as they could remain in one another's company he was supremely content and happy.

Hans, when they explained the Frenchman's presence, was the first to raise the question as to whether they should carry their weapons down with them into the town or leave them here in the house. It would, he said, obviously be the wisest course to present themselves unarmed. They didn't want any accident at the last moment. Sergeant Karol agreed but Peter didn't trust the Frenchman. He could possibly be armed, Peter said, and might seek a reward if he shot them in the back and claimed them as prisoners who had resisted.

"We'll take a chance on that," said Sergeant Karol. "We're four to one anyway, but we'll leave our weapons in the cellar where you found the potato. And we'll see that our French friend goes ahead of us." Sasha and Karl took the tommy-gun and the three rifles down below and then the five of them set off, with the Frenchman leading along the road to Rapoltsveiler. They walked in silence for the most part because now that the die was irrevocably cast there was a certain feeling of humiliation, since they had all been soldiers, and for one of them at least it was the second time he had been deprived of his firearm in which he took such pride.

A quarter of a mile from Rapoltsveiler a footpath led across a meadow in a short cut and this they followed in the same order, with the mud in places oozing over their boots. In a few minutes they reached another road and the Frenchman turned to the left again. All this time they had encountered no one and doubts were stealing into Sasha's mind when the jeep came round the corner.

It was travelling very fast with two young American soldiers in the front seat. At the sight of the party coming down the road the American who was driving pulled up so suddenly that his companion was flung violently forward; then both men were out on the road with their pistols in their hands.

"Get your hands up over your heads, before they get nasty," said Sergeant Karol.

They raised their hands and the Americans came swiftly down the road with their weapons levelled. They searched each

310

man for arms, and satisfied that they possessed none offered a cigarette. Then the sign language began all over again,

Sasha puffed away at his cigarette and let the others get excited. Hans and Peter gesticulated wildly and the Frenchman did his best with both arms while Sergeant Karol looked on with cynical indulgence. The two Americans, who were both surprisingly young and unbelievably clean in these circumstances of war and weather, leaned against the jeep whither they'd led their prisoners and grinned to their hearts' content. It was all a very happy little party with nobody achieving anything, but conducting themselves like old friends, when the American officer and another enlisted man came down the road.

"Quick, throw your cigarette away," said one of the Americans, and then because nobody understood a word and there were strict orders regarding fraternization, he snatched the cigarette from Sasha's lips and trampled it into the mud.

The officer came to a halt by the jeep and the talking began all over again but the officer had a few words of French. Within a little time he was in the jeep with the two Americans and driving back to the house to collect the weapons in the cellar, and Sergeant Karol with the others were marching into Rapoltsveiler.

An hour later together with twenty other prisoners of war they were on their way to Epinal. Ten hours after that they were given their first square meal, a meal of the American special issue of dry hydrated tinned rations. Twelve hours later in a convoy of lorries, over one thousand prisoners of war were bound for Besançon.

Hans and Peter, in the confusion had been lost to the party of four, but Sasha and Sergeant Karol remained.

6

"Now this is the thing to do," said Sergeant Karol. "And make sure you understand. I've had a chance to speak with one of the others and he says we shall be sorted out at Besançon. He speaks a bit of English and got it all from one of the Americans. They'll ask you at the Besançon transit centre what your nationality is. Where they send you next depends upon your answer. If you say you're a Byelorussian they may repatriate you. If you go back home you know what awaits you, with the Russians in occupation ... So what you do is say you are a Pole. It's the safest bet. Don't let them mention repatriation, and anyway if the war ends soon, which I think it will, you don't know who will be waiting for you on your own doorstep, so keep clear till things settle down. Therefore you volunteer to serve with any branch of the Polish forces who are attached to the Allies. That is what I intend to do. And you do the same. Understand?"

"Yes," said Sasha. They were seated with twenty or more other prisoners on the floor of a lorry in the Besançon convoy. They were still half an hour from their destination. Twice when passing through French villages on the long journey from Epinal the population had staged hostile demonstrations, attempting to clamber aboard the lorries when they had been at a standstill and drag the German prisoners down amongst a ferocious crowd in order to lynch them. And once an American guard, exasperated and indignant, had fired a burst of a dozen rounds over the heads of the mob to disperse them, growling under his breath: "In 1940 they wouldn't fight. But now they can afford to be brave."

"Yes, I understand," said Sasha in reply to Sergeant Karol. "But I wonder what Colonel Shaeffer would say if he heard we intended going over to the British."

"The trouble with you, 'kutscher'," said Sergeant Karol, "is that you suffer from ideals. You always did. I suppose that's why I like you, as personally I've never possessed any in my life. As for Shaeffer, he was a fine man but he's not my commanding officer any longer nor anyone else's, which shows the advantage of being a sergeant who is alive compared to a dead colonel."

"Do you remember the day you ordered me to shoot that Partisan and I refused?" said Sasha.

"Very vividly. I ought to have shot you."

"Do you think they will let us stick together?"

"I don't see why they shouldn't," said Sergeant Karol. "At least I'll do my damndest to try and see that they do."

"That's good," said Sasha. "I don't mind what Colonel Shaeffer thinks of me now."

"You're a funny kind of boy," said Sergeant Karol. "Did you ever hear any more of that brother of yours, the one I heard about — the Partisan?"

"Not a word," said Sasha.

"That's bad. Does it worry you much?"

"It used to. It's not been so bad lately."

"You get accustomed to losses," said Sergeant Karol.

"It's not that. It has been easier since we came across from the other front —"

"Easier!"

"As regards Nicola. When we were hunting the bandits round Radzimichy I'd often wonder if a bullet of mine had killed him. That couldn't happen in Alsace. Besides —"

"Besides... well?"

"Oh nothing," said Sasha.

"I wouldn't have minded having a kid brother like you," said Sergeant Karol.

"You've been a good friend to me," said Sasha. "You gave me a start when I was a 'kutscher' and you saved my family from the Gestapo and me from the gas-chambers at Dachau. And you stood up for me at Rapoltsveiler."

"That's nothing," said Sergeant Karol. "As one pal to another. Now when we detrain stick close to me and we'll live to fight another day. Never say 'die'."

"Never say 'die'," said Sasha.

There were huts in row after row behind the wire at Besançon. They jumped down from the lorries as they stopped beyond the cordon and the barrier, and stood nearby, till the American officers with their sergeants managed to produce some sort of order and form them into lines. The guards on the perimeter were coloured troops.

Sasha kept close to Sergeant Karol because it was unthinkable that they should be separated after all they had gone through together. It seemed to Sasha that perhaps what God took away with the one hand, He gave back with the other. It wasn't anybody's duty to question the rightness of that. Nicola perhaps — though God forbid! — had gone for ever. Sergeant Karol in time could almost take his place.

There was considerable confusion in the camp because events had moved very fast and the prisoners were pouring in, convoy on convoy. The immediate necessity was to sort them out in their various categories of nationality and rank, age and religion. As each contingent came in the sorting out began. In long lines they filed through the various huts and completed the "pro-formas" handed to them giving the required details.

314

Sasha, fast on Sergeant Karol's heels, filled in his forms and with great earnestness under the column "Nationality" wrote with the stub of the pencil provided on a length of string the word "Polish." In the "Remarks" column he added, "I wish to volunteer for the Polish Army."

It was quite astonishing to think that a few simple words might change anyone's life so completely. Admittedly this was only the beginning and he would have to wait for an acceptance from the Polish authorities, nevertheless it could mean the beginning of a new life. Sergeant Karol had said the war was coming to an end and now anyway for the time being, both of them were out of it. It wouldn't be too bad being a prisoner of war because he'd have Sergeant Karol alongside of him and they would become very great friends indeed. "As one comrade to another," Sergeant Karol had implied. That was a very satisfying sentiment to hear expressed. Comrades in arms, that's what they were of course, just as all the others had been, and now the last few weeks had seen that comradeship ripen and come to fruition.

Somewhere a bugle began to blow, whistles were shrilling and orders being shouted. There was a concerted movement down the length of the long hut towards the door at the far end, where the guards stood. An American officer was shouting directions in German and repeating them in Polish. The great mass of prisoners jostled each other, struggling to keep their places, behind them fresh arrivals pressed forward. Sasha could see Sergeant Karol in quarter profile as he himself fought his way towards him. Somebody stumbled and another prisoner moving across his path took his place. Sasha could see only Sergeant Karol's shoulder now, and then a man twice his size, a giant of a man, blundered into him and Sergeant Karol was lost to view.

The press of bodies, slowly moving forward, was suffocating. Sasha thought he had never encountered so many people in so small a space. He was utterly powerless to move in any other direction but that which the crowd was slowly and relentlessly taking. He could see no farther ahead than the next man's back, nor could he raise his arms, pinned close to his sides, as he was carried along. Then on a sudden as the heaving body of men emerged from the hut he found he could walk on his own again. He staggered and nearly fell and then like a rock in a torrent an American coloured guard, with the insignia of the military police, split the tide in two.

He stood with three others immediately behind him, four stalwarts with their white, steel helmets and their black faces shining with sweat, separating the tide of humanity to left and right. Sasha clawed at the arm of one of them but he was swept past.

"I have a friend ... he is a sergeant ... we are to stick together... Let me get to my friend ..."

He had little idea what he was saying. The only thing he knew was that he must find Sergeant Karol before they were irrevocably separated.

"My friend, the sergeant ... he can't be more than a few yards away ..."

He was speaking in his native tongue, incoherently, wildly. He must reach Sergeant Karol before it was too late, but the crowd was thinning now and there was nobody in sight who was in the least like his friend.

The white-helmeted guard hustled him on and he found himself in a line of men. It was beginning to rain and a spot fell on his face. He started forward to expostulate, to explain, to plead with the officer who had suddenly appeared from nowhere and was taking charge. Then the line was forming into a column and it was beginning to march, taking him with it.

It was no good pleading with them. They didn't know what he was talking about and he knew that if they had known they wouldn't have cared. He was only as one grain of sand on an immense foreshore. Whatever life might have held for him within one man's heart it was now irretrievably lost. He plodded on with bowed head.

7

The overcrowded cattle-truck contained forty men. They were all Poles and prisoners of war. The story went that the train carried at least a thousand men, so it was understandable that it was hardly possible to sit down. It was also said that they were bound for the big camp down south at Marseilles and that seemed likely enough by the time they were taking. They had been aboard for three nights and two days now. The food consisted of the American tinned ration, and a bucket of water was supplied for each truck which had a sergeant, prisoner of war, in charge. The trucks had been padlocked before they started and the train had only stopped once outside a station. No arrangements had been made for relief of the person. Prisoners urinated through a crack in the planking and defecation must be made on to old newspapers provided for that purpose and then parcelled and flung through the open windows.

The sound of the train as it went along seemed to Sasha's ears to chant a rhythm, "*Sergeant* Karol... *Sergeant* Karol... *Sergeant* Karol," when it was grinding up an incline, and when it gathered speed, "*Nicola — Nicola — Nicola... Nicola — Nicola — Nicola.*" He felt the double loss to be irreparable. Every mile that the clattering wheels covered added to the great distance between himself and home. Very soon the distance would be so great that all thoughts of ever returning could be dismissed. The turning of his coat had all seemed rational and right when his friend had been with him; now he wasn't so sure. His conscience pricked him when he thought of his dead colonel. Then he thought of Radzimichy again and the village of

Dubrova and was forced to realize that even if he had the good fortune to return and escape the Russian vengeance, that there might be nothing to go back for but a heap of rubble and a handful of ashes.

He stood in his corner of the swaying, jolting cattle-truck and the stench of human bodies with their stale perspiration and the ammonia and tang of urine had become so familiar that he knew that he was scarcely noticing it. There was an irritation under his arms and in his crutch. He supposed that like the majority of them he was going lousy. He didn't care. He didn't care about anything any more. There was nobody left now. He was indeed alone. The wheels went clattering on.

They arrived at Marseilles at two o'clock in the afternoon and detrained into lorries, driven by American coloured troops. It was cold and raining. The prisoners sat on the floor, huddled together, glum and disconsolate. Nobody seemed inclined to talk, as they were driven along the sandy roads and sometimes across open country. The tented camp was ten miles from Marseilles and situated in the middle of a field. Coloured troops guarded it, patrolling the perimeter wire or keeping watch from their wooden towers. The prisoners were driven past the barrier and got out of their lorries. It was raining more heavily than ever.

A rough road ran through the centre of the camp. On the left and right were the rows and rows of tents and half-way down the track, stood the four check huts. Part of the medical staff had been posted from Besançon. Sasha recognized some of them when he went in for inspection after filing through the other huts on the old rigmarole of date of birth, place nationality and religion. It was Besançon all over again. They told him that there were no lice on him, so he supposed it must have been his imagination. Then everyone was assembled in drill order, allocated to a tent, marched across the road and dismissed. There were eighteen men to a tent. In the tent to which he had been allotted there were already twenty.

He stood outside the tent with two Poles and a Byelorussian and the dusk came down with the rain. In a little time the prisoner in charge of the tent came out, went across to the kitchen in the right-hand corner of the wire perimeter, drew his tent's rations and returned. He gave Sasha his allowance of a slice of bread and butter and half a billy-can of coffee.

"I'm sorry," he said, "that there's no room inside for you. But I daresay the rain will stop later on."

Then he went into the tent and laced the flap tight to make sure.

There was a hollow in the ground big enough to take four men, not very far away from the wire. Sasha still had with him the blanket that Sergeant Karol had given him on the first night march from the barrier on the road to Rapoltsveiler. He made his way to the hollow and the other four followed him. Then he curled up in his blanket and tried to sleep. He had no intention of becoming sociable and entering into conversation until he was sure of his company. He would take every care not to disclose his true nationality.

It was almost impossible to sleep and for a time he listened to the fitful conversation of his companions, one of whom had already spent two days in the camp in the open. He learnt that the camp was packed to overflowing with German prisoners including a section put aside for Poles only, and that the two Poles present had volunteered, like himself, for the Free Polish Army. They discussed their chances and the time that might elapse before they received any news. Nobody seemed to know anything at all definite and in time he dozed off, only to wake a couple of hours later chilled through with the cold. So in such a manner alternately sleeping and waking in a nightmare of discomfort, the night passed. When morning came he was more stiff and sore than if he had marched through the long and dreary hours.

He returned to the tent to which he had been allotted and the same prisoner in charge fetched the rations from the cook-house and shared them out. He received another slice of bread and a teaspoonful of marmalade. He was becoming ravenously hungry and his bowels rumbled ominously.

At ten o'clock in the morning the whole camp paraded and the lists for the day were read out by the American officer in charge. As a man's name was called he answered to it and fell out on the left. In a little time some fifty out of seven hundred men had fallen out and formed a detachment on their own. He learnt that they were the lucky ones who had been accepted by the Polish Army and would leave that day. He wondered if his own turn would ever arrive.

The midday meal showed some small improvement, being composed of vegetable soup and a few pieces of horse meat in it. But the irritation on his body began again and the more he thought about it, the more insistent it became so that he wondered if the doctors had been over-casual in their cursory examination and determined to explore for himself. Having no desire to advertise his discomfort, he made his way down the line of tents and towards the wire. The day had brightened but his heart was heavy within him. He felt he could have made up for the lack of last night's sleep if only his flesh would stop creeping. He sat down on a patch of dry sand near the wire and removed his shirt.

He began to search the seams because it was there, if there were any, lice would be found. He remembered how Papa who had been in the First World War had told him that interesting fact and how he had burnt the vermin out by applying the burning end of a cigarette. The only trouble, of course, was that he had no cigarette. He pressed open the seams of a sleeve and ran his thumbnail along it. The whole business so disgusted him that in exasperation he flung his shirt from him. At precisely the same moment came the violent report of a rifle shot close at hand, while the sand spurted up between his feet. He seized his shirt and scrambled to his feet.

There were two guards the other side of the wire. One still held his rifle to his shoulder aiming at Sasha's legs and the other, his eyes boggling in his coal-black face and his white teeth flashing, was frantically waving Sasha away from the wire and at the same time shouting. Then a voice behind Sasha said:

"Get back away from the wire. Don't you know the regulations?" He turned to find a young man in the tattered uniform of a legionnaire standing a dozen paces away from him.

"You're not allowed within twenty-five yards of the wire. Keep away from it or you'll get shot."

Shirt in hand, Sasha hastily retreated. Satisfied, the two guards moved away.

"You're very lucky you didn't get killed," said the stranger. "They shoot first and ask the questions afterwards in this camp. Haven't I seen you before somewhere? Weren't you one of Colonel Shaeffer's battalion at Vesoul? My name is Symon Veter, what's yours? I'm a Byelorussian."

"Sasha Nioman. I seem to recognize your face."

"Yes. We never met, but you were in the massacre, weren't you? I remember the parade at Lomza when the colonel shook you and the others by the hand. You slept out all last night, didn't you?"

"Yes," said Sasha with a sour look and putting on his shirt. "And very unpleasant it was."

"I thought of you several times during the night. I said to myself, 'I know that chap'," said Symon Veter. "That fellow in charge of the tent — he's no good. I'll see that there's a place for you tonight. That's why I followed you along. I'll fix it."

"That's very kind of you," said Sasha.

"Well, you're a bit of hero, aren't you? We've got to look after them. What's happened to Colonel Shaeffer? I've been away sick and then I was caught just outside Rapoltsveiler."

"The Colonel's dead," said Sasha. "Killed in the fighting round Altkirch."

"I'm sorry. He was a great gentleman and a fine soldier. Though he never shook *me* by the hand. What happened to you?"

"We were surrounded and cut off. I gave myself up, with a friend. I feel a bit ashamed. I think we should have fought our way out."

"What with? A couple of tommy-guns against a tank? Don't be silly."

"My friend persuaded me and now I've lost him. We got separated at Besançon. In a way I wish that bullet had hit me just now."

"In my home at Minsk," said Symon Veter softly, "We had a motto hung up in the parlour and my father often used to point to it. He died after a Gestapo beating. A friend betrayed him. But the motto read: "Money lost, little lost. Honour lost, much lost. Heart lost, all lost." That motto's worth thinking about."

"We had a saying in my platoon like that," said Sasha. "It's not the same as yours, and yet it is. 'Never say die'. I think I was in danger of forgetting it. That's two things I have to thank you for, Symon Veter."

"That's all right. When you get in the tent tonight, if you must talk, speak Polish. I don't want them to think I am a Byelorussian. I've volunteered for the Polish Army."

"So have I," said Sasha eagerly. He was recovering his spirit already. "Do you think we stand a chance? Will it be long before we get a decision?"

"You can't tell," said Symon Veter.

They fell to talking about their chances, and from that to comparing notes of old friends they had known when the battalion was fighting round Radzimichy. Symon had been in the action on the Dvina and remembered little Symon Ravin and the occasion when he had gone out with Sasha to try and get Paval Kaluta safely back. And in the evening Symon broached the subject of making room for his new friend in the tent, and after a fierce argument succeeded in persuading the prisoner in charge that a place must be found. So that was the end of the first day in the tented camp near Marseilles.

A fortnight passed. The monotony was irksome and the food was scanty. Once Sasha did a turn in the cook-house, which was a popular move amongst the prisoners as there was always the chance of picking up a spare crust. Sometimes he wondered if good news would ever come through. Each morning the parade took place and the lists were read out, but neither his name nor that of Symon's was shouted. It was getting towards the last weeks of December.

Then on the morning of Christmas Eve, 1944, both his name and Symon's were called.

8

He lay on the floor of the forward hold of the French cargo vessel *Bel Aurore* with his precious blanket around him. The converted troopship with three hundred ex-prisoners of war was steaming for Taranto in Italy. He was posted to the 2nd Corps of the Polish Army, together with Symon Veter. They had now been at sea for forty-eight hours of the three days' trip and it had been blowing a gale ever since they had left Marseilles. He had been extremely sea-sick and there had been several casualties aboard with the heavy seas running. The "heads" consisted of a couple of buckets on the deck and there was only one safety-line so that any one could be washed overboard or flung against the rails. Several men had broken their ribs staggering against some obstruction on the perilously slanting deck. He had begun to think it was the very hell of a way to spend Christmas.

But what did it matter? Ever since Symon Veter had gently taken him to task he had regained his customary courage. Life couldn't stop because he had lost some friends; and now that he was quit of the tedium and semi-starvation of the tented camp his spirits had risen.

It would all come out in the wash. That was the old catchword. If he had survived so much, surely there could be so much more worth surviving, *and he wasn't seventeen and a half years old yet.* So therefore what he must do, he told himself, was to look forward and never backwards; and if he was never to see the old, loved familiar faces again, then he must be prepared to accept the fact as God's will.

Only it wasn't easy. It was very hard. It was going to take all his courage to face the new life ahead.

They disembarked at Taranto, and Polish transport driven by Polish A.T.S. drove them to Yolande Camp. There they were paraded given a two-man tent, a pair of blankets, and a palliasse. They put up their tents in a camp filled with Poles captured from the German Army. There had been heavy casualties amongst the Free Poles in the recent Italian campaign and they were only too glad to reinforce their ranks even if the newcomers had been fighting on the wrong side! Anyway, the Free Poles reassured themselves, that it hadn't been these newcomers' fault if they had been put in such a position that they'd had no choice but fight for the Germans; and if some of them were Byelorussians posing as their own countrymen who was to know the difference as long as no awkward questions were asked? Therefore in a short time they directed Sasha to the quartermaster's store, took his German uniform away and gave him a British battle-dress. With his slight, trim figure which he always carried very erect he looked very well in it. He hoped he could be a credit to the British Army of which he was now a part.

9

He walked smartly past headquarters at Yolande Camp. He had just been told he was posted to the 15th Tank (Polish) Regiment in South Italy. He felt the cup of his happiness was very full. He was a free man amongst free people. He hoped death wasn't waiting round the corner after everything that had happened. He wanted to enjoy this new-found freedom and relish it.

Somebody he seemed to know was coming towards him. He was tall and slim and about thirty; and his eyes were of a bright brown, so that when he smiled it looked as if there were little gold flecks flashing in them. He was smiling now, as one brother might smile to a younger brother who has been lost and found.

"So I got here first," said Sergeant Karol, holding out his hand. "But you've found your way."

"Yes," said Sasha, gripping Sergeant Karol's hand. "I've found my way, at last."

PART FOUR: AT PEACE WITH THE WORLD

1

They had been married a whole year now and there was a new baby. They had called it Nina. And there was another little girl — a stepdaughter, called Christine. Mary, Sasha's wife had her hands full with the children and keeping house for Sasha. The house was a two-room flat in Brighton and the year was 1956. At times Sasha felt the war was a very long time ago and at other times only yesterday. Now, drowsing over the Sunday papers on the verandah it seemed that it was only the other day that he had left Yolande Camp to join the 15th Tank (Polish) Regiment in Southern Italy, but in reality it was just on eleven years ago. From that day of departure he had never seen or heard of Sergeant Karol again; but he knew that Nicola was alive, so the wound had healed. From there they had sailed for Egypt for tank-training and had remained in the Canal Zone till the September after the end of the war, then they returned to Italy again and carried out guard duties on British stores.

In June, 1946, they had left Italy for Scotland, arriving at Glasgow and then they had been posted to Browning Camp, at Horsham in Sussex, awaiting demobilization. He had grown to love the Sussex Downs and the green fields because they were reminiscent of Radzimichy and Dubrova and all who had lived there, Mamma, Papa, Nicola, Walter and Valia. He had sworn that when the war was over he would settle in England if they would have him. Twice in 1947 he had been in touch with his family. There had been an exchange of a couple of letters from Nicola, who had survived the war. He had been wounded with the Partisans and had spent ten months in hospital and in the second letter there was news of Walter's marriage; but later letters had been terse and reading between the lines he had sensed the tension in which they had been written, so he himself had thought it wiser to close the correspondence until such a time as his family felt it safer to write more openly. But since then there had been silence.

So when the war had ended he had stayed in England and had gone to London, living in a hostel. He had worked for two years as a builder's labourer with one firm and then gone to another in the same capacity till 1950. And after that there had been various jobs, such as the one in a toy factory at Chiswick, then on to a firm of corrugated cardboard carton makers, and then to Manchester as show-room assistant in Rootes.

In March, 1955, he had gone to Paris to join the Foreign Legion but had failed his medical. He'd been stranded in France with no money, but the British Embassy, on the security of a cousin in Manchester, had arranged for a passage back to Newhaven. He had arrived with two pounds in his pocket after selling his watch at Sainte Lazare to a French ticket collector. Then because this was Sussex and one choice was as good as another, he had taken a Number 12 bus to Brighton and discovered a room for twenty-five shillings a week.

He had been determined not to ask anyone for help and after a week found a job as a house-porter at the Royal Albion Hotel. He had stayed for a while and then on a hotel guest's advice went over to Hollingbury where there were factories. He had worked as a labourer but he'd left before Christmas because they wouldn't put him on to a machine. He felt he was as good as the others and resented the decision, but he had met Mary there.

He had gone to Crawley after that and found work again as a labourer at Gatwick Airport with the Wade Engineering

Company; then they had put him on the machines, and that had suited him fine. All the time he had kept up a correspondence with Mary. She, too, had been lonely. The Wade Engineering Company moved to Brighton, and he had gone along with them. They seemed to be satisfied with him because they had given him more money. Then he'd asked Mary to marry him. They had married in August, 1955. Now they had a two-roomed home of their own, of which he had done all the painting and decorating. It was on the ground floor of a big house and the verandah by the window looked out over the garden. On a warm afternoon like this he would often doze in his chair. He was at peace with the world.

2

Mary came to the door that opened on to the verandah. She had put on her apron because there was the washing-up to do.

"Wake up," she said. "There's work to do."

Sasha got up out of his wicker-work chair. One leg had been broken off short so he had propped it up with a book.

"I must mend that chair one day," he said.

"What a way to use a book," said Mary. "I read something the other day which a man called Housman wrote. I copied it out. I think if you put 'legionnaires' instead of 'mercenaries' it might apply. I'll fetch it, you can get started."

She brought the scrap of paper into the kitchen.

"It's good, isn't it?" she said.

He read:

"These, in the day when heaven was falling,
The hour when earth's foundations fled,
Followed their mercenary calling
And took their wages and are dead."

"Their shoulders held the sky suspended;
They stood, and earth's foundations stay;
What God abandoned, these defended,
And saved the sum of things for pay."

"Yes," said Sasha. "It's very good. I like it."

A NOTE TO THE READER

If you have enjoyed this book enough to leave a review on **Amazon** and **Goodreads**, then we would be truly grateful.

The Estate of Anthony Richardson

Sapere Books is an exciting new publisher of brilliant fiction and popular history.

To find out more about our latest releases and our monthly bargain books visit our website:
saperebooks.com

Printed in Great Britain
by Amazon

38017981R00185